Pan Study Aids

Geography
1
Physical and Human

E. W. Young

Pan Books London and Sydney
in association with **Heinemann Educational Books**

First published 1980 by Pan Books Ltd,
Cavaye Place, London SW10 9PG
in association with Heinemann Educational Books Ltd

ISBN 0 330 25969 5

Printed and bound in Great Britain by
Richard Clay (The Chaucer Press) Ltd, Bungay, Suffolk

PAN STUDY AIDS

Titles published in this series

Biology
Chemistry
English Language
Effective Study Skills
Geography 1   *Physical and Human*
Geography 2   *British Isles, Western Europe, North America*
Maths
Physics

Forthcoming titles

Book-keeping and Accounts
Commerce
Economics
French
History 1   *British*
History 2   *European*
Human Biology

Brodies Notes on English Literature

This long established series published in Pan Study Aids now contains
more than 150 titles. Each volume covers one of the major works of
English literature regularly set for examinations.

Contents

Acknowledgements

The publishers are grateful to the following Exam Boards, whose addresses are listed on page 6, for permission to reproduce questions from examination papers:

Associated Examination Board, University of Cambridge Local Examinations Syndicate, Joint Matriculation Board, University of London Schools Examination Board, Northern Ireland Schools Examination Council, Oxford Delegacy of Local Examinations, Oxford and Cambridge Schools Examination Board, Scottish Certificate of Education Examining Board, Southern University Joint Board, Welsh Joint Education Committee.

To the student

Before you read this book make sure you understand what it can (and cannot) do for you.

It *cannot* take the place of good textbooks and an atlas, and it cannot help you to pass examinations without hard work. It *can*, however, help you to make the most effective use of your time, both before and during the examination.

Geography is now so vast a subject that no O level syllabus covers more than a small part of it, yet each syllabus calls for a wide range of knowledge and understanding. As its name suggests, this book can guide your study so that you will concentrate your efforts on those parts of the subject most likely to be tested; you will practise the skills needed in the examination; you will familiarize yourself with the various forms of question you are most likely to meet; and you will make your revision really constructive by relating it to a selection of such questions taken from the examination papers.

The Exam Boards

The addresses given below are those from which copies of syllabuses and past examination papers may be ordered. The abbreviations (AEB, etc) are those used in this book to identify actual questions.

Associated Examining Board,   (AEB)
Wellington House,
Aldershot, Hants GU11 1BQ

University of Cambridge Local Examinations Syndicate,   (CAM)
Syndicate Buildings, 17 Harvey Road,
Cambridge CB1 2EU

Joint Matriculation Board,   (JMB)
(Agent) John Sherratt and Son Ltd,
78 Park Road,
Altrincham, Cheshire WA14 5QQ

University of London School Examinations Department,   (LOND)
66-72 Gower Street,
London WC1E 6EE

Northern Ireland Schools Examinations Council   (NI)
Examinations Office,
Beechill House,
Beechill Road,
Belfast BT8 4RS

Oxford Delegacy of Local Examinations,   (OX)
Ewert Place,
Summertown,
Oxford OX2 7BZ

Oxford and Cambridge Schools Examination Board,   (O & C)
10 Trumpington Street,
Cambridge CB2 1QB

Scottish Certificate of Education Examining Board,   (SCOT)
(Agent) Robert Gibson and Sons, Ltd,
17 Fitzroy Place,
Glasgow G3 7SF

Southern Universities Joint Board,   (SUJB)
Cotham Road, Bristol BS6 6DD

Welsh Joint Education Committee,   (WEL)
245 Western Avenue,
Cardiff CF5 2YX

1 Preparing for the examination

You are probably reading these words because you are preparing to sit a GCE O level examination. If you are studying on your own it may be that you do not know full details of what is expected of you. Make sure of these details without further delay.

Ten different examining bodies (for simplicity called 'Boards' in this book) offer syllabuses in geography at O level. They are listed opposite. Some Boards offer more than one syllabus in geography. Decide at once, if you have not already done so, which syllabus you propose to follow. Obtain a copy, and copies of question papers for the past two or three years. Note any changes proposed for the year in which you will be taking the examination. Check also, without delay, the last dates for entry, the fees payable and the dates of the actual examination.

Compare your syllabus in detail with the contents of this book, of the second book on geography in this series (*Geography: 2 British Isles, Western Europe, North America*) if you have it, and of your textbooks. Make sure you know where to look for material on each topic. The syllabus will probably include some alternatives. Note carefully the 'either/or's and decide firmly which you are choosing. Check the question papers to see how the alternatives are reflected in the form of the paper. You will find that even if you cover more than the minimum requirement you may have no opportunity to display your wider knowledge because the instructions will prevent you from doing so.

Study the way in which the question paper is set out. Some layouts are very clear, with headings indicating the different sections of the syllabus. Others are simply an unbroken list. In such cases you will still find a regular pattern: eg one question each year on climate, one on landforms, one on farming, and so on.

Field studies

Almost all syllabuses include one or more questions on 'a small area of which you have made a special study', or some similar phrase. Such an area may be in a town or in the country. This book does not attempt to cover the topic of field studies because the necessary techniques cannot be satisfactorily learnt and practised except through an outdoor course under skilled guidance.

If time allows you to take such a course before the examination, you will find it both interesting and helpful. If you have left school, inquiries about courses suited to your needs may be addressed to your local College of Further Education or education office, or to the Geographical Association, 343 Fulwood Road, Sheffield S10 3BP.

If you have had experience of field work, use it as widely as possible in the examination. It will have thrown a new light on many aspects of physical and human geography, and an examiner cannot help being favourably impressed when a candidate supports his statements with examples clearly based on first-hand knowledge.

Background reading

In the few months before the examination you may have little time to spare for any but essential reading. Try all the same to follow the news, and make notes of facts and events which will provide useful examples.

Many such points may relate to disasters such as earthquakes, famines, floods and droughts. Where exactly have they occurred, and why there? Other news stories or television documentary programmes may concern, for example, important new mineral discoveries, arguments about the siting of a new airport, or plans for redeveloping part of your local town. All such matters can be related to the geography syllabus. All help to give life to textbook generalizations.

Using this book

Having identified the chapters relating to your syllabus, work through them in a definite order. They will give you a sound framework, which must be filled in with further reading from one or more good textbooks. Almost a hundred actual examination questions are included. Prepare full, or at least outline, answers to as many as possible; this sort of work is much more stimulating and fruitful than simply reading and re-reading. Make sure also that you can answer the minor questions in the text.

Many words are printed in bold type, **like this**. They vary in importance, but all are words that you must know and understand. Keep a list of any that are not already familiar, and write against each one a note of its meaning. Re-read the list from time to time until you really know it.

The maps and diagrams have been deliberately kept simple. Use them as models, and practise until you can draw them quickly *and* accurately. Colours are a valuable aid to constructing effective maps and diagrams, but in the examination room you will have no time for 'decorations'. Use colours, therefore, to distinguish one feature from another: latitude from longitude, roads from railways, coastlines from isotherms, and so on. Colour shading, eg for relief, is a good thing, but keep it light. Blue seas are a waste of time.

Various suggestions are made, especially in Chapter 6, for making your own maps from data provided. This again is a constructive form of revision, active rather than passive. What you draw or write, as well as read, will be imprinted much more deeply on your memory.

Equipment
To do yourself justice in the examination room you need adequate (but not elaborate) equipment. This should include:

> H and HB pencils; good quality eraser (rubber);
> coloured pencils – red, blue, green, brown;
> fine-point fibre pens – black and red – for lettering;
> compasses, dividers, protractor, setsquare;
> reading lens for close and quick study of the
> OS map extract; ruler (metric markings).

Needless to say, thorough practice is needed in the use of all these aids to help you produce clear and accurate work.

Another essential item is the atlas. Various firms – Philip, Oxford University Press, Collins-Longman, Bartholomew – publish atlases very suitable for O level work. Make sure that yours is at your elbow, and preferably open, whenever you are working.

The question paper
Look quickly through this book and note the various forms in which O level questions (printed here in italics) are set. Notice in particular how few of them require an essay-type answer. With the exception of SUJB and LOND, single-sentence questions are extremely rare, and questions in six or eight parts are quite common. This makes your task in the examination much simpler, provided you read the questions carefully. To do this may take a few precious minutes, but it is time well spent. Using a past paper, practise the following drill:

1 Look first at the **rubric** (instructions) at the head of the paper. Check the time available and the number of questions to be done.

2 How many sections are there, and how many questions must you, or may you, attempt in each section? Remember – you will gain no credit for questions you fail to answer, or for those you answer from the wrong section.

3 Look through the sections that concern you, and put a line through those questions you cannot attempt. Look carefully at the rest, and when you are sure you have understood them (the longest questions are often the easiest to answer) make your choice.

4 Before starting each one, check the wording again. 'Choose TWO of the following . . .' or '. . . examples drawn from outside the British Isles . . .' – phrases like these are instructions, not polite requests. 'Describe and account for . . .' sets you two different tasks; *both* must be done. 'London *or* Paris . . .' does not mean 'London *and* Paris . . .'

Do not be afraid to make rough notes before starting to write. Jot down the points your answer must cover, and put a line through them as you deal with them. The examiner will be only too happy to disregard anything you have crossed out.

As we have seen, few questions call for more than a paragraph or so to each part. Do not 'waffle' – the examiner will not be impressed. Remember that he or she is a busy person with several hundred scripts to mark in a short time, and will not happily read four pages of irrelevant padding in order to unearth three relevant facts. So set out what you know in simple terms, clearly written and correctly spelt. Take trouble, in particular, with geographical words. By writing (eg) 'Britian' or 'Antartic' you will irritate rather than impress the examiner.

Textbooks

In several chapters of this book mention is made of the increasing tendency to base questions on photographs, usually of landforms, urban or rural landscapes and farming activities. Whether in books, filmstrips or elsewhere, you should find and study photographs covering these topics, preferably accompanied by text which analyses and explains the photographs.

Geography is well catered for by many good textbooks, but the following are written from the same 'self-help' point of view as this book, and are copiously illustrated. They can be borrowed through your local library or obtained from any bookseller.

Young and Lowry, *A Course in World Geography* (Edward Arnold)
- Book 3   *Regions of the World: Their Work and Wealth*
- Book 10   *The World: a Systematic Geography*

E. W. Young, *Basic Studies in Geography* (Edward Arnold)
- Book S2   *The Scenery of Britain in OS Maps and Photographs*
- Book S4   *The Earth as a Setting for Human Life*
- Book S5   *Farming, Fishing and Forestry*
- Book S6   *Power, Mining and Manufacturing*
- Book S7   *Settlement, Trade and Transport*

Some references to specific chapters in this book may be helpful:

Ch. 2   CWG3, ch. 1; CWG10, ch. 1; S4, pp5–21
Ch. 3   CWG10, chs. 2 and 3; S2 (all); S4, pp44–53
Chs. 4 and 5   CWG3, ch. 1; CWG10, chs. 4 and 5; S4, pp22–43, 56–61
Ch. 6   CWG3, chs. 6,7,9,10; S5, pp54–66; S6, pp12–17, 28–41
Ch. 7   CWG3, chs. 2,3,4,5,8; CWG10, ch. 6; S6, pp4–53
Ch. 8   CWG3, ch. 11; CWG10, chs. 8,9,10; S7, pp4–27
Ch. 9   CWG3, ch. 10; CWG10, ch. 7; S6, pp42–63; S7, pp28–63
Ch. 10   S2 (all)

Multiple-choice questions

Some Boards include a whole section or paper of this type of question, often based on a world map and testing, among other topics, the sort of fact covered by the map overleaf, which you will be well-advised to know by heart.

These questions are designed to test quickly a wide range of fairly general knowledge and an understanding of the principles involved. Examples will be found on pp15, 90–91 and 112.

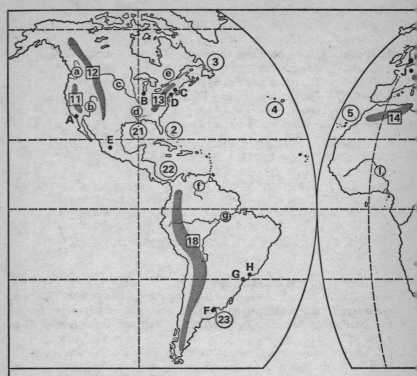

WORLD REVISION TEST MAP

Five sets of features are marked on this map by letters and numbers and listed below, **but not in the same order**. Write lists **A** to **T**, **a** to **u** and **1** to **29**, and insert the names you know. Check the rest. Repeat at intervals until you know them all. Identify also the seven lines of latitude and longitude marked by pecked lines.

Cities over 5 m population (lettered **A** to **T**). See also *Book 2* p. 144.		Islands (**1** to **10**)	Mountains (**11** to **20**)
Bangkok	Moscow	Azores	Alps
Bombay	New York	Canaries	Andes
Buenos Aires	Paris	Cuba	Appalachians
Cairo	Peiping	Japan	Atlas
Calcutta	Philadelphia	Java	Drakensberg
Chicago	Rio de Janeiro	Malagasy	Gt. Dividing
Djakarta	Sao Paulo	(*Madagascar*)	Range
London	Seoul	Newfoundland	Himalayas
Los Angeles	Shanghai	New Zealand	Rockies
Mexico City	Tokyo	Philippines	Sierra Nevada
		Sri Lanka	Urals

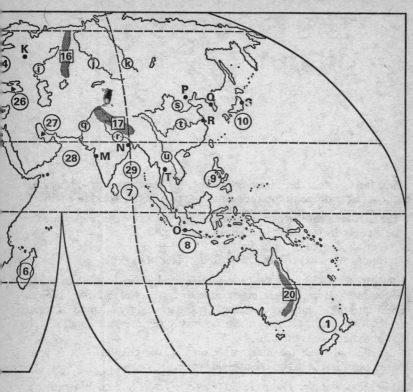

Sea areas
(21 to 29)
Arabian Sea
Baltic Sea
Bay of Bengal
Black Sea
Caribbean Sea
Mediterranean
 Sea
Gulf of Mexico
Persian Gulf
Rio de la Plata

Rivers
(a to u)

Amazon	Indus	Orange
Colorado	Mekong	Orinoco
Columbia	Mississippi	St. Lawrence
Congo	Missouri	Volga
Danube	Niger	Yangtze
Ganges	Nile	Yenisei
Hwangho	Ob	Zambesi

2 The Earth as a planet

Three facts explain the changing seasons, the varying length of day and night, and the difference in time from one part of the world to another:

1 the Earth is a **satellite** or **planet** of the sun, round which it travels **in orbit** once in $365\frac{1}{4}$ days (one **solar year** – p20);
2 it is an almost perfect sphere;
3 it rotates on an **axis** tilted at $66\frac{1}{2}°$ to the plane of its orbit.

A firm grasp of these topics is essential to an understanding of world geography. You must therefore be able to answer the following typical recent questions and part-questions (wording slightly adapted in some cases). Notice how many of them positively require part or all of the answer to be in diagram form.

Attempt all these questions after reading the chapter. Check your answers against the list on the opposite page.

1 *For the city of Sao Paulo (23°30′ S, 47°W) state and explain with the aid of diagrams:*
   (a) local time when it is noon (GMT) at London;
   (b) the elevation of the noonday sun on 21 December;
   (c) the length of daylight hours on 21 March. (LOND)
2 *(a) When it is midday at Manaus, Brazil (60°W), what time will it be at London?*
   (b) Show with the aid of diagrams why the Tropic of Cancer is $23\frac{1}{2}°$ North of the Equator.
   (c) At what angle do the Sun's rays strike the Earth at noon on 21 December at Tomsk, USSR (56°30′N)? (SUJB)
3 *(a) Explain why the Equator always receives equal amounts of daylight and darkness, while the Poles can receive 24 hours of daylight and 24 hours of darkness at different dates.*
   (b) By means of a labelled diagram only, explain what you understand by longitude.

(c) *Explain the significance of the* **International Date Line** *for a person crossing the Pacific Ocean from California (120°W longitude) to Japan (135°E longitude) and later returning in the opposite direction.*   (WEL)

4 *Of the following sentences, underline the one which describes the difference between the local times of New Orleans (90°W) and Cairo (30°E):*

The time at New Orleans is 4 hours behind that at Cairo.

The time at New Orleans is 8 hours behind that at Cairo.

The time at New Orleans is 8 hours in advance of Cairo.

The time at New Orleans is 4 hours in advance of Cairo.

Both New Orleans and Cairo have the same time.   (OX)

Answers

1 (a) Adapt diagram p22 to show only two meridians – 0° and 47°W.
Explain that local time is :
($4 \text{ minutes} \times 47$) = 188 mins = $3 \text{hrs } 8 \text{mins}$ = $3 \text{hrs } 8 \text{mins}$ *earlier than* GMT ... local time = 0852.

(b) Adapt diagram (b) on p21 and mark Sao Paulo on the Tropic of Capricorn. Explain that for this reason the midday sun is vertically overhead there on 21 December.

(c) Draw diagram p20. State that on 21 March (the *autumn* equinox in Sao Paulo) daylight there *and throughout the world* is 12 hours. Add reasons (text p21).

2 (a) Be careful! – most such questions are based on noon at Greenwich. Draw diagram much as in 1(a) above, and calculate GMT as *later than* Manaus time. *Answer* 1600 h (4 pm).

(b) Adapt diagram (a) p21. Explain what the Tropic of Cancer represents (text p16) and show in the diagram that $90° - 66\frac{1}{2}° = 23\frac{1}{2}°$.

(c) See diagram (b) p19 and accompanying text.

3 (a) Draw diagrams (a) and (b) p21 and briefly state what each one shows about the length of daylight. Point out that the day/night line *always* bisects the Equator.

(b) Diagram p17 with concise 'labels' based on the text.

(c) Draw a simple sketch-map showing Japan, USA, the IDL and two labelled arrows, one for each journey. Explain briefly that the westward journey involves 'losing' a day, which is regained by 'repeating' a day on the return journey.

4 Working shown on p22. Underline the second choice. (This is a typical 'multiple-choice' question – see p11.)

HOW LATITUDE IS CALCULATED

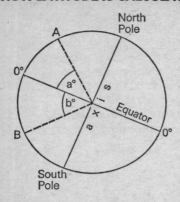

The **latitude** of a point on the Earth's surface is its distance N. or S. of the Equator, measured as an angle at the Earth's centre and varying from 0° (the Equator) to 90° (the North and South Poles).

This diagram represents the Earth sliced in half through the Poles. The latitude of point A is *a*°N, while point B is *b*°S.

Latitude

The only fixed points on the turning Earth are the two ends of its axis – the **Poles**. Points midway between the Poles lie on the Equator – an imaginary line which divides the Northern and Southern **Hemispheres** and forms a base line for the measurement of latitude.

Any line joining points of the same latitude forms an east-west circle parallel to the Equator. Such lines are called **parallels** of latitude. Four parallels have a special significance:

1 the **Arctic Circle** (66½°N) marks the limit of the area round the North Pole within which, in each year, there are at least twenty-four hours continuous darkness and at least twenty-four hours continuous daylight.
2 the **Antarctic Circle** (66½°S) marks the limit of the corresponding area round the South Pole.
3 the **Tropics of Cancer** (23½°N) and
4 **Capricorn** (23½°S) are (respectively) the most northerly and southerly latitudes at which the noonday sun stands vertically overhead at least once in the year. Between these two lies the area generally referred to as 'the tropics'.

Satisfy yourself, from the diagrams overleaf, that in each of these four cases you understand the statement made.

Practise drawing all the diagrams in this chapter *accurately*; eg the Earth's axis must be at 90° to the plane of the Equator and the day/night line must exactly bisect it.

HOW LONGITUDE IS CALCULATED

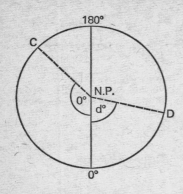

The longitude of a point on the Earth's surface is its distance E. or W. of the **Prime Meridian** (see below) measured as an angle at the Earth's axis.

This diagram represents the Earth as viewed from above the North Pole. The longitude of point C is c°W, while point D is d°E.

Longitude

At right angles to the parallels of latitude runs another system of lines. These join the North and South Poles and are called **meridians of longitude,** and they form a means of calculating distance east and west. For this to be possible, however, there has to be a starting point of 0° – a **prime meridian** – accepted by all concerned. For historical reasons the longitude of the former Royal Observatory at Greenwich in London is accepted as such worldwide. The 'Greenwich Line' is thus shown in the diagram above, as in all atlases, as 0°. Note that whereas latitude is calculated from 0° to 90°, longitude is calculated from 0° to 180°.

Taken together, latitude and longitude lines form coordinates by which the position of any point on the Earth's surface can be identified very precisely. Atlas indexes normally quote latitude and longitude to the nearest **minute of arc** ($\frac{1}{60}$ of a degree) and you should practise finding places by this means. Britain's **National Reference Grid** (*p147*) is based on latitude and longitude.

Great Circles

Any line dividing the Earth exactly in half (eg the Equator, or the circle formed by the meridians of 90°E and 90°W) is called a **Great Circle.** The shortest route between any two points on the Earth's surface lies along the Great Circle which passes through them. That is why intercontinental air and shipping routes often follow courses which appear odd when set out on a flat map.

A LATITUDE AND THE SUN'S ALTITUDE

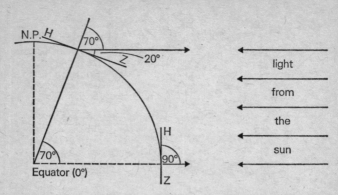

The **angle of elevation** of the noonday sun above the horizon (HZ) is related to the latitude of the observer. Notice that the huge size and distance of the sun from Earth means that its light reaches the Earth in parallel rays.

The measurement of the angles is thus a matter of simple geometry. When the noonday sun is overhead at the Equator, its altitude at any other point *on the same meridian* is the complement of the latitude; ie altitude = 90° – latitude.

Latitude and the sun

The diagrams on p21 show that at any moment half the Earth is in sunlight and half in darkness. Because of the Earth's rotation, most points on its surface move into sunlight for a part of each twenty-four-hour period (although there are some very important exceptions to this – see pp20–21). Halfway through this sunlight period is midday – **local noon** – when the sun appears at its highest (for that day) in the sky. (*NB* this does NOT mean it is vertically overhead. It may be so, or it may not; this depends on (a) the time of year and (b) on the latitude of the place in question.)

Study diagrams (A) and (B) carefully and test your understanding by constructing a third diagram to show the midday sun's altitude at Tomsk on 21 June, when it is overhead at the Tropic of Cancer, 23½°N. It should be clear from your diagram that the answer is:

90° – (*difference* of latitudes) ie 90° – (56½° – 23½°)
= 90° – 33°
= 57°

B LATITUDE AND THE SUN'S ALTITUDE

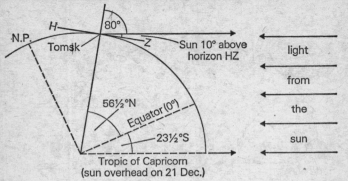

The conditions shown in (A) exist only twice a year. At other times the sun is overhead at some point north or south of the Equator.

This diagram illustrates Q2(c) on p14 and shows that when the sun is overhead at a point in the southern hemisphere, its altitude at a place in the northern hemisphere is the complement of the *sum* of the latitudes of both places.

Thus the sun's altitude at noon at Tomsk on 21 Dec. will be:
$90° - (56\frac{1}{2}° + 23\frac{1}{2}°) = 90° - 80° = 10°$

C LATITUDE AND INSOLATION

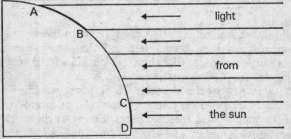

The same amount of sunlight is falling on the land surface AB as on CD.

This diagram explains why latitude is a vitally important factor in determining the climate of any place. Where the sun is always high in the sky at midday its effective energy (**insolation**) is concentrated much more closely than in high latitudes (ie nearer the Poles).

THE SUN'S ORBIT AND THE SEASONS

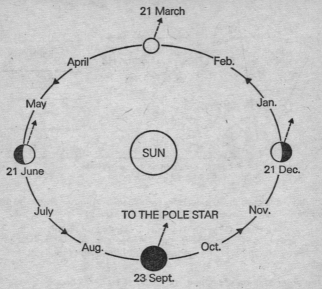

Notice that the tilt of the Earth's axis is always in the same direction, so that the North (or South) Pole is inclined sometimes towards and sometimes away from the sun, while twice a year neither Pole is inclined towards the sun.

Check from the diagram, and write down, the dates of these four positions.

The seasons

Near the Equator the noonday sun is always high in the sky, month-by-month temperatures vary very little, and the terms 'summer' and 'winter' have little meaning. Elsewhere seasonal change is very marked, and the diagram above sums up the reasons.

From April to August the Northern Hemisphere is inclined towards the sun, so that (see previous page) it receives more intense insolation. It also enjoys longer days (see opposite). For both these reasons the mean temperature is higher, and growing conditions (in respect of light and warmth) are better, than from October to February. In the Southern Hemisphere the reverse dates apply.

In June the overhead sun is at its furthest north ($23\frac{1}{2}°$) after which it appears further and further south until in December it stands at $23\frac{1}{2}°S$. From December to June it moves northward. This annual swing is called the **apparent migration of the overhead sun.**

THE VARYING LENGTHS OF DAY AND NIGHT

A 21 June – Sun overhead at 23½°N   **B** 22 Dec. – Sun overhead at 23½°S

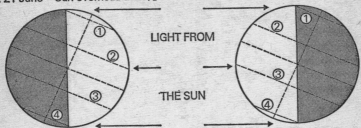

LIGHT FROM

THE SUN

At Equator: *12 hours daylight*

Everywhere in N. Hemisphere:
more than 12 hours daylight

At 66½°N, and thence northwards:
24 hours daylight

At the N. Pole: *midway through
6 months continuous daylight*

At Equator: *12 hours daylight*

Everywhere in N. Hemisphere:
less than 12 hours daylight

At 66½°N, and thence northwards:
24 hours darkness

At the N. Pole: *midway through
6 months continuous darkness*

Day and night

Even in a small country like Britain, the summer days and winter nights
in northern Scotland are noticeably longer than in southern England.
These two diagrams, illustrating the summer and winter **solstices**, are
enlarged from the opposite page and show why latitude, as well as time
of year, affects the length of day and night. Check both diagrams,
preferably with the help of a globe, and make sure you understand how
they explain the notes beneath. As a further check rewrite the exercise
in relation to the Southern Hemisphere.

What names are given to the four parallels of latitude numbered in
the diagrams? See p16 if you have forgotten.

We are all familiar with the slow annual change from 'shortest day'
to 'longest day' and back again. Halfway between each solstice, in March
and September, the Earth reaches a point in orbit where the tilt of its
axis is neither towards nor away from the sun (*diagram opposite*). The
noonday sun is overhead at the Equator, the boundary between light
and darkness passes through both Poles, and the whole Earth has equal
periods of daylight and darkness. These two dates are the **equinoxes**.

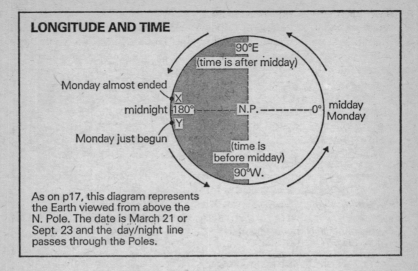

LONGITUDE AND TIME

As on p17, this diagram represents the Earth viewed from above the N. Pole. The date is March 21 or Sept. 23 and the day/night line passes through the Poles.

Longitude and time

The Earth rotates through 360° in twenty-four hours (ie 15° in 1 hour, or 1° in 4 minutes).

Remember that the four meridians of longitude shown in this diagram are curved lines on a sphere and not straight lines on a flat circle. When it is midday at Greenwich it is also midday at any other point on the meridian of 0° – 'meridian', in fact, means 'midday line'. (*If this is not clear from the diagram, check on a globe.*)

At the same moment it is midnight at all points on the 180° meridian. At places east of Greenwich the time is already past midday – their **local noon** is earlier. At places west of Greenwich local noon on any given day is later.

Thus, if we know the longitude of two places we can calculate their difference in **local time** (and vice versa; navigators check their longitude by comparing their time with the Greenwich time signals).

Questions on this topic are most easily dealt with by drawing a simple diagram based on the one above. In Q4 on p15 the diagram would show clearly that the two places were (90°W – 30°E) – 120° apart, so that the time difference is 120÷15=8 hours.

Be careful not to confuse or misread E and W longitudes (eg if these places had been at 90°W and 30°W, the answer would have been 90° *minus* 30°=60° (or four hours in time)).

The International Date Line

Look again at the diagram opposite. At point X it is already almost Tuesday; at point Y Sunday has only just ended. There is a whole day's difference between two places quite close together, and if no adjustment were made there would be worldwide confusion about dates, timetables, and so on.

The 180° meridian is accepted as the **International Date Line**, except for local deviations to avoid inhabited areas. Check these deviations in your atlas, and note that fortunately the 180° line lies almost entirely across open ocean.

The effect of the IDL is clear from the diagram:

1 crossing the Line from east to west (Y to X) travellers 'lose' a day – ie the calendar moves one day forward.
('Going west, a day goes west.')
2 crossing from west to east (X to Y) travellers 'gain' a day. In this example, Monday is repeated.

This rather confusing topic is rarely tested except at the simple level of Q3(c) on p14. The key point to check is – Does the specified journey involve crossing the IDL, and if so, in which direction?

Standard time, and time zones

Differences in local time have been explained opposite. These differences are quite noticeable, even within a small country. Land's End is almost 6° west of Greenwich, and so local noon there is over twenty minutes later than in London.

For each part of Britain to set its clocks exactly by the sun would, however, be hopelessly confusing. For convenience we accept the time at Greenwich as **standard time** for the whole country. Indeed, **Greenwich Mean Time** (GMT) has become the basis for timekeeping in almost every part of the world, just as the Greenwich Line is accepted as the Prime Meridian for the measurement of longitude.

Since 15° of longitude represent one hour's difference in local time, most really big countries divide their territory into Time Zones about 15° wide. Each zone has a standard local time one hour different from its neighbours and ahead of, or behind, GMT by one hour for every 15° of longitude. The USSR has eleven such zones, the USA (including Alaska) seven and Canada six. Your atlas probably includes a world map showing these divisions.

3 Landscapes and landforms

Landscapes vary from place to place because of:

1 the differing nature of the rocks beneath the soil;
2 movements within the Earth's crust;
3 **denudation** – shaping of the land surface by different natural forces.

The result is a variety of **landforms** – the detailed features of the landscape. A thorough knowledge of these landforms is essential. Even if your syllabus does not include a section on physical geography, the OS map question will almost always assume some familiarity with the material in this chapter.

Rocks and landforms

It is important to remember that the term **rock** includes all mineral substances that form part of the Earth's crust. Sand, shingle and clay are rocks, just as much as granite and limestone. Rocks are often classified by age, as shown by the **fossils** they contain. A simpler classification is by origin, ie by the manner in which they were formed. The notes opposite cover a number of typical questions. Other questions may test your understanding of the particular landforms associated with different types of rock:

5 *Name* three *types of sedimentary rock. Choose* one *of these and describe the landforms commonly associated with it.*   (OX)

A similar question might be set on igneous rocks. From this chapter and from your textbook prepare answers to *both* questions. These should include sketch-maps, diagrams and, wherever possible, named examples. You may be asked to identify landforms from photographs and/or OS maps (note p151 and booklist p11).

The principal types of rock (according to their origin)

Igneous ('*fire-formed*') **rocks** The Earth's inner crust, only a few kilometres beneath our feet, is so hot that the rocks are soft and plastic. This molten material (**magma**) sometimes burns its way through the overlying crust, often along lines of weakness such as **faults** (p32). Eventually it cools and hardens in two distinct forms:

1 **Intrusive rocks,** in or between the layers of previously-existing rocks. Because it is still buried, the magma cools slowly and the crystals of each mineral it contains have time to form and grow separately. This accounts for the mottled appearance of (eg) granite.

2 **Extrusive** (or **volcanic**) **rocks,** which have reached ground level before solidifying. Because they have cooled quickly they show little crystallization and are therefore fine-grained (eg basalt) or even like glass (eg obsidian). In extreme cases the magma solidifies before giving up the gases it contains, and so has a spongy appearance (eg pumice).

Sedimentary ('*laid down*') **rocks** Every type of rock begins to be worn away as soon as it is exposed on the Earth's surface. The resulting rock waste is carried away and deposited somewhere else (*diagram p35*) as layers of **sediment**. The sediment may be finely or coarsely broken down, and may contain very different mixtures of minerals. In most cases the material is eventually cemented or compressed into **strata** (beds) of solid rock (eg sandstone, clay).

An important group of sedimentary rocks is formed from organic deposits. Limestones (including chalk) derive from the remains of marine life. Coal derives from vegetation which was sealed from the air by layers of mud or sand, and which solidified under great pressure instead of decaying in the normal way.

Metamorphic ('*changed in form*') **rocks** **Pressure** from overlying strata or from movements within the Earth's crust; or **heating**, by pressure or by flows of igneous rock; or **chemical action** by gas or water within the crust: all these may alter the nature of either sedimentary or igneous rocks. Usually the result is to harden the original rock. Clay may become slate, limestone may become marble, granite may become gneiss.

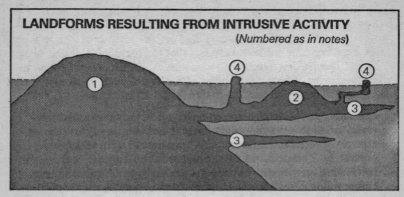

LANDFORMS RESULTING FROM INTRUSIVE ACTIVITY
(Numbered as in notes)

Vulcanicity

This term includes all the processes by which magma, gas or steam intrude into or emerge from the Earth's crust. It is a favourite topic with examiners. A typical question is:

6 *Write an account, illustrated by examples, of igneous activity and volcanic landforms.*   (LOND)

Igneous activity – intrusive (*see diagrams, numbered as here*)

1 A **batholith** is a large mass of igneous rock formed by a deep-seated intrusion of magma. When the surface rocks have been eroded (eg along the broken line in the diagram) the batholith stands out as an upland or mountain mass (eg Dartmoor, Mont Blanc).

2 A **boss** is smaller but similar in origin.

3 A **sill** is a near-horizontal (tabular) sheet of magma intruded between existing strata. The Whin Sill in Northumberland, on which a part of Hadrian's Wall was built, is a well-known British example at ground level.

4 A **dyke** is a more-or-less vertical intrusion cutting through existing strata, often along the line of a fault.

Igneous activity – extrusive (volcanic)

Volcanoes are of several types, but all consist of igneous material ejected through a vent in the crust.

5 A **shield volcano** is formed by very fluid basic lava which spreads out widely before it solidifies. Mauna Loa on Hawaii stands 10km above the ocean floor, but its base is 500km across.

6 A **lava flow** of similar material, welling out from one or more fissures rather than from a single vent, may cover vast areas to depths of thousands of metres. The Deccan in India and the Antrim

EXTRUSIVE (VOLCANIC) LANDFORMS
(Numbered as in notes)

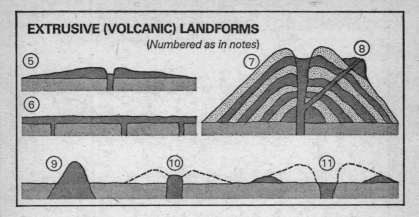

Plateau in Northern Ireland, which ends in the Giant's Causeway, are well-known examples.

7 Acid lava is more viscous, ie it does not flow so freely, and so builds a steeper **cone**. Because it solidifies quickly, thus tending to block the vent and cause a build-up of pressure, eruptions are often violent and even explosive, as when Vesuvius overwhelmed Pompeii in AD 79. This type of volcano also throws out cinders and 'ash' – powdered lava – and often builds a **composite cone** made up (as shown) of alternate layers of lava and ash.

8 A very active volcano may have **secondary** or **parasitic cones**.

9 Very viscous lava may build up the extraordinarily steep-sided cones known in France as **puys**.

10 Is not a puy, but a **plug** of very hard lava remaining after the cone which once held it (broken lines) has been eroded away. Edinburgh Castle stands on a plug.

11 Violent eruptions sometimes blow away most of a cone, leaving a depression or **caldera** which may be ten or more kilometres across. Secondary cones may reform inside this ring, which may also contain a **crater lake**.

Hot springs and **geysers** (intermittent eruptions of steam or boiling water) are milder forms of vulcanicity, usually found where the actual volcanoes are **extinct** (no recorded eruption) or dormant (no recent eruption).

Copy the diagrams and study them carefully in conjunction with the notes. Revise the topic later by answering the question (*opposite*) from the diagrams alone, and then comparing your answer with the notes.

PRINCIPAL 'PLATES' AND PLATE BOUNDARIES

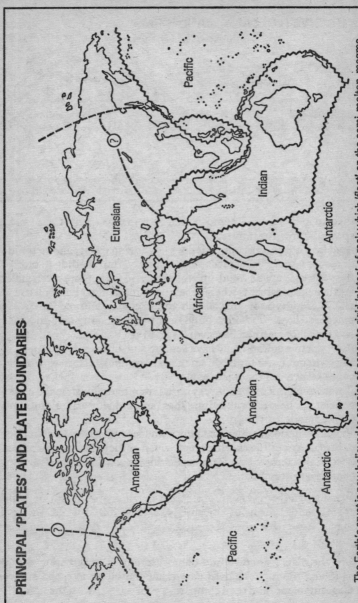

The Earth's crust is now believed to consist of separate rigid 'plates' of rock which 'float' on the semi-molten magma below. Moving at perhaps five millimetres per year, they pull apart or push together or grind alongside each other with results suggested in the diagram (*see also Book 2, p104*).

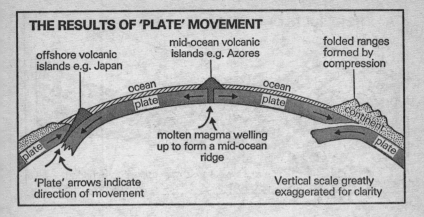

THE RESULTS OF 'PLATE' MOVEMENT

offshore volcanic
islands e.g. Japan

mid-ocean volcanic
islands e.g. Azores

folded ranges
formed by
compression

ocean

plate

ocean

plate

continent

plate

plate

molten magma welling
up to form a mid-ocean
ridge

'Plate' arrows indicate
direction of movement

Vertical scale greatly
exaggerated for clarity

Movements within the Earth's crust

Find a textbook or atlas map of volcanic and **seismic** (earthquake) activity throughout the world. Make a list of the locations of earthquakes and volcanic eruptions which you have read or heard about, or which occur while you are studying for this examination. Compare the map and your list with the test map on pp12–13, which show the major ranges of high mountains.

These mountains are high because they have not yet been worn down by erosion; therefore they are 'young' (as geologists reckon time). So many of them are associated with earthquakes and volcanoes that they are clearly in an unstable condition. They are, indeed, still in process of formation.

Over the centuries men have tried in various ways to explain these lines of instability in the Earth's crust. Only in the past few years has a theory been put forward which is acceptable to most scientists. This is the 'plate' theory outlined here in the diagram and world map. It is so new a theory that your textbook may not mention it, and a summary is given here because it helps in an understanding of many puzzling features of the Earth's surface.

How, for example, can the summit of Everest be formed of sedimentary rock which was clearly laid down in a deep sea? The answer must allow for very great movements within the crust. Many striking landforms are produced by the **folding** and **faulting** involved in these crustal movements.

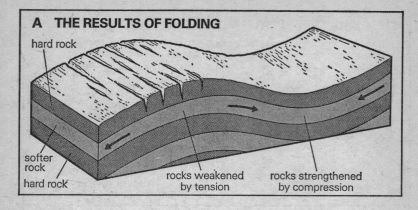

A   THE RESULTS OF FOLDING

hard rock

softer rock

hard rock

rocks weakened by tension

rocks strengthened by compression

Folding and faulting are among the most frequent topics for questions on any syllabus which includes physical geography, but the questions are almost always quite simple, eg:

7 *Write an account, illustrated by examples, of folding and faulting.*   (LOND)

8 *For each of: intermontane basin; rift valley:*
  (*a*) *name an example and describe its characteristic features;*
  (*b*) *suggest reasons to explain the formation of these features.*   (AEB *adapted.*)

Folding
Any type of rock may be subjected to folding, but the results are seen most clearly in the case of gently folded sedimentary strata of varying hardness, as in diagrams (A) and (B). Remembering that erosion begins to wear down a land surface as soon as it emerges above sea level, compare the two diagrams and note carefully how (B) develops from (A).

Identify the following formations in (B), and make sure that in each case you understand the process of formation:

1 **Anticline** – an upfold in a bed or series of beds of rock.
2 **Syncline** – a downfold.
3 **Dip slope** – the tilted surface of a folded bed.
4 **Strike** – the direction at right angles to the dip.
5 **Scarp slope** – the exposed edge of a bed of rock after uplifting, folding and erosion.
6 **Cuesta or escarpment** – the ridge formed by a scarp slope and a dip slope.

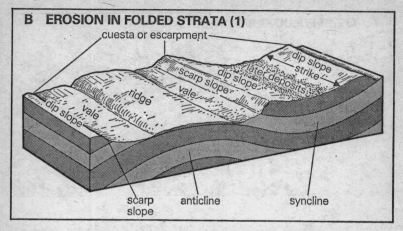

B   EROSION IN FOLDED STRATA (1)

cuesta or escarpment

dip slope
strike
scarp slope
dip slope
later deposits
ridge
vale
dip slope
vale

scarp slope   anticline   syncline

What is the source of the material forming the 'later deposits' in (B)?

Suggest, from (A) and (B), why an anticline is normally eroded faster than a syncline. You should give three reasons, each incorporating one of the following phrases: **lines of weakness/greater exposure to the forces of erosion/protected by later deposits.**

State in simple words how, after millions of years, the land surface might be as shown in (C). Explain the wording of the diagram. A well-known example of this landform is Snowdon.

Remember – diagrams of this type are inevitably much over-simplified. You should word your answers on such topics to show that you realize the size (many thousands of metres high, many hundreds of kilometres across) of great mountain ranges, and the length of time (scores of millions of years) involved in their formation and destruction.

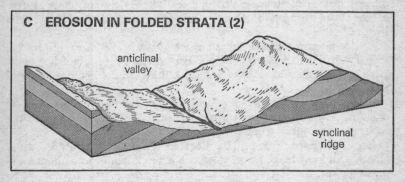

C   EROSION IN FOLDED STRATA (2)

anticlinal
valley

synclinal
ridge

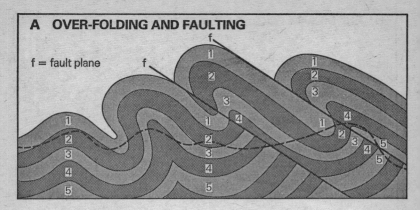

A OVER-FOLDING AND FAULTING

f = fault plane

Faulting

Great thicknesses of rock can be folded to an astonishing extent without breaking the continuity of the different strata involved. Beyond a point, however, the strain can only be relieved by complete fractures. These **faults** allow one mass to slide over or past another as in diagram (A).

Trace the diagram, omitting all details above the broken line. Your new diagram will show how and why, in a region like the Alps, the surface rocks may vary greatly in type and age within quite short distances.

In some regions faulting is the principal means by which strains within the Earth's crust are relieved. Diagram (B) illustrates various ways in which, over a long period, this may happen. The movements may be only a few millimetres or (rarely) a metre or so at a time, but the resulting vibrations cause shock waves in the surface rocks over a wide area which we experience as earthquakes. The violence of an earthquake seems out of all proportion to the small amount of movement usually involved.

Faults are responsible for some of the world's most impressive scenery, such as the Rift Valley of East Africa or, on a smaller scale, Giggleswick Scar and other very steep hillsides in the Pennines (*Book 2* p11).

The presence of faults is not always obvious, however. As shown by diagram (C), erosion carves away the sharp outlines even while the faults are shaping the scenery.

Copy and learn diagram (B). Locate the examples in a good atlas. Check your knowledge by naming each lettered landform without looking at the key.

B TYPES OF FAULT

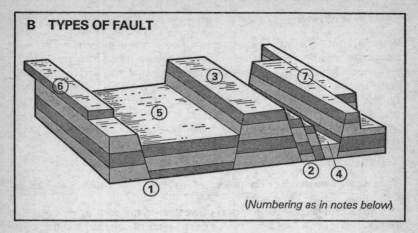

(Numbering as in notes below)

Vertical movements produce:
1 simple fault. 2 step fault (two or more faults with varying amounts
of movement). **3 horst** or **block mountain** (eg the Black Forest of
southern Germany, the Vosges of eastern France, the Sierra Nevada of USA).
4 rift valley (eg the Central Lowlands of Scotland, the Jordan Valley, the
middle Rhine from Bingen to Basle). **5 intermontane basin** (eg the Great
Basin of Utah, USA).

Lateral (sideways) movements produce:
1 thrust fault (as in diagram (a)). **2 tear fault** (eg the San Andreas
fault, California, USA (*Book 2*, p104); the Great Glen, Scotland, between
Fort William and Inverness).

C THE SCENERY OF A FAULTED REGION

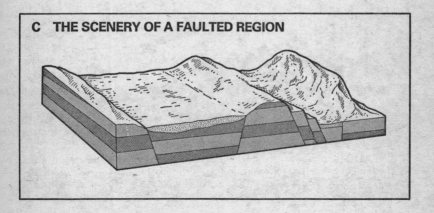

Denudation

The four previous pages have shown how crustal movements which shape the broad outlines of the landscape are balanced by forces which reshape and eventually destroy it. Make sure that you understand and can describe in simple terms the four-stage process illustrated below, by which an existing rock surface is converted into material for the formation of new rocks.

On the first stage, this typical half-question can be answered from the notes opposite:

9 Describe the nature and results of weathering.   (LOND)

Your answer must cover the processes involved ('the nature') as well as the visible effects ('the results').

The second stage – the removal of weathered material by erosion – is sometimes very slow; in such cases deep layers of soil may build up. In other cases erosion is so effective that no soil has time to form. Sooner or later, though, every land surface is stripped and lowered by running water, ice or wind, or by a combination of these three **agents of erosion** which are also agents of transport and deposition.

The distinctive features of soil formation and of the work of each agent of erosion, together with the type of examination question to be expected, are reviewed in sequence on pp35–55. It must be remembered, however, that all four stages of denudation are taking place at the same time, and virtually all the time.

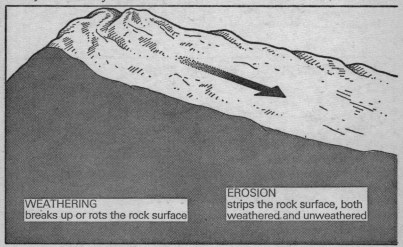

WEATHERING
breaks up or rots the rock surface

EROSION
strips the rock surface, both weathered and unweathered

Weathering

Mechanical weathering   (a) **Frost-shattering** or **freeze-thaw**: on mountain sides, and wherever the temperature oftens falls below freezing, moisture in rock crevices freezes and expands. As a result the widened crevices now hold more water, which again freezes and expands, forcing them wider still. Large and small fragments eventually break or flake off and fall away to form scree on the slopes below. (b) **Change of temperature**: where the **diurnal range of temperature** (p60) is very wide, or where showers of rain fall on overheated rock surfaces, the outer layers often crack or flake off (**exfoliation** or **'onion-skin weathering'**). This is because the minerals composing the rocks expand and contract at different rates and thus split apart. On steep slopes, scree is formed as in (a).

Chemical weathering (rock-rotting)   Some rocks (eg limestone) are composed of minerals which dissolve in water. This process is much more effective when the water is salty, or warm, or polluted by industrial fumes. Thus a rock may slowly waste away, or decay into a different form as (eg) decayed granite leaves a residue of kaolin (china clay). Action of this sort affects rock far below ground level.

Organic weathering   Plant roots penetrate cracks in solid rock and break it up as effectively as frost. Decaying plant and animals remains produce acids which rot the solid **bedrock** beneath the soil.

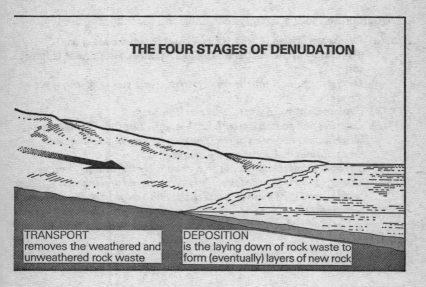

THE FOUR STAGES OF DENUDATION

TRANSPORT removes the weathered and unweathered rock waste

DEPOSITION is the laying down of rock waste to form (eventually) layers of new rock

Soils

Except on the highest mountains and in the driest deserts, the rock waste produced by mechanical weathering is gradually changed by chemical and organic weathering into **soil** – a complex material capable of supporting plant life.

How well the soil can do this – ie how fertile it is – depends partly on the amount of **humus** (decayed organic material) it contains, partly on the nature of the chemicals in the rock particles, and partly on the climate.

One way of distinguishing soils is by their **texture**. Coarse-grained soils are **sands**, finer soils are **silts**, and the smallest particles, so densely packed as to be impervious to water, form **clays**. Most of us are familiar with the difference between 'light' (sandy) and 'heavy' (clay) soils, and with the way in which each responds to different weather conditions. Clearly the type and quality of the soil is a vital factor in the farming of any region.

Where soil has lain undisturbed for a long period, three layers (**horizons**) may often be distinguished by their colour and form. They are known as the A, B and C horizons, as in the diagram on p37 showing a **soil profile** typical of English deciduous woodland. Where the soil is saturated, either continually or seasonally, the chemical nutrients in the A horizon are washed down into the lower layers. This process, which of course leaves the surface soil less fertile, is called **leaching**.

Questions on soils are rarely searching, and the following are typical:

10 (a) *On the world map . . . shade and locate the main areas of one named* important temperate soil *and one named* important tropical soil.

   (b) *Describe and explain the characteristics and causes of the types of soil named in* (a).   (LOND)

11 (a) *Explain what you mean by the term 'leaching'.*

   (b) *Laterites and podsols are both leached soils. List* four *differences between these two types of soil. You may include in your answer the conditions under which they are formed.*

   (c) (i) *Name a soil which has not been excessively leached.* (ii) *Locate an area where it may be found.* (iii) *With the aid of a labelled profile describe its main characteristics and explain how it may have been formed.*   (CAM)

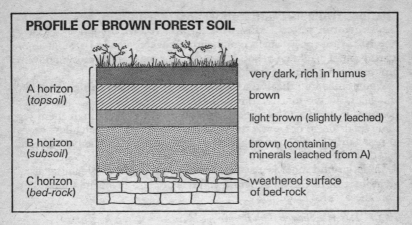

PROFILE OF BROWN FOREST SOIL

A horizon (*topsoil*)
- very dark, rich in humus
- brown
- light brown (slightly leached)

B horizon (*subsoil*)
- brown (containing minerals leached from A)

C horizon (*bed-rock*)
- weathered surface of bed-rock

Zonal soils (ie soils developed in particular climatic regions) include:
1 **Brown forest soils**, formed under deciduous forest in mild or warm temperate conditions, as in northwest Europe. (See diagram and draw corresponding labelled diagrams for the other three examples.)
2 **Podsols**, formed in cold temperate regions, eg the coniferous forests of North America and Asia (p88). Vegetation decays slowly in this climate, so that humus is generally lacking. Melting snow every spring causes heavy leaching. Except in a very thin surface layer the A horizon is ash-grey, sour and infertile. The B horizon contains so much leached material, including particles of clay, that drainage may be poor.
3 **Chernozem** ('black earth'), formed in the temperate grasslands of middle-latitude interior regions, eg the steppes of the USSR and the prairies of North America. The warm moist summers encourage grass growth, but are not so wet as to leach the resulting humus. The A horizon is deep, passing from an extremely dark, rich surface layer down into a thinner and paler B horizon.
4 **Laterite**, formed in hot, high-rainfall equatorial regions. Vegetation decays so rapidly in this climate that humus is leached almost as fast as it forms. The A horizon is deep, consisting of dark, red, porous (and therefore dry) soil which is very infertile, grading imperceptibly into the B horizon.

Azonal soils Many surface deposits have been laid down so recently that they have not been much modified by climate, and show no ABC profile. Examples are: **boulder clay** (p50), **alluvium** (p46).

Erosion, transport and deposition by running water

Underground water   Most land surfaces receive moderate or heavy precipitation (p64). Surface moisture (a) evaporates or (b) sinks in or (c) runs off. Together, (b) and (c) account for most of the erosion now in progress throughout the world.

Water sinks into the surface rocks if they are **permeable,** ie if they will allow water to pass through them. Permeable rocks are either **porous,** with air spaces which allow water to soak through them (eg some sandstones) or **pervious,** with joints or cracks which allow water to pass fairly freely (eg carboniferous limestone). Chalk is both porous *and* pervious.

Underground water is associated with some very special landforms of great interest in British geography. They are also favourite topics with examiners, as for example:

12 (a) *Describe the relief and drainage of an area of chalk upland.*
   (b) *With the aid of labelled diagrams explain the occurence of the following features in areas composed mainly of chalk: (i) springs; (ii) dry valleys.*
   (c) *Name four features of a carboniferous limestone upland which are not usually found in a chalk upland.*   (CAM)

Chalkland scenery   Chalk occurs in very thick strata. Water sinks into and through it with little erosive effect. Chalk is, however, soluble in water, especially as water becomes slightly acid after passing through the soil. This accounts, at least in part, for the typical gently-rounded outline of the chalk strata that stand out quite prominently as the Chilterns, the North and South Downs and other well-known English uplands. Make sure you can mark them all on an outline map.

Question (b)(ii) above cannot be fully explained, since experts differ as to the way in which dry valleys have been formed. Possible explanations include:

1 Scarp crest once stood higher – dip slope streams cut valleys which are now 'beheaded' ?
2 Climate once much wetter, so water table formerly higher ?
3 Ice sheet (*see p50*) may have blocked normal drainage from scarp foot, 'ponding' it back until the overflow cut channels through the scarp crest ?
4 Chalk remained frozen, and therefore impermeable, long after the ice sheet melted, so streams eroded the surface instead of sinking into it ?

DRAINAGE AND LANDFORMS IN A CHALK CUESTA

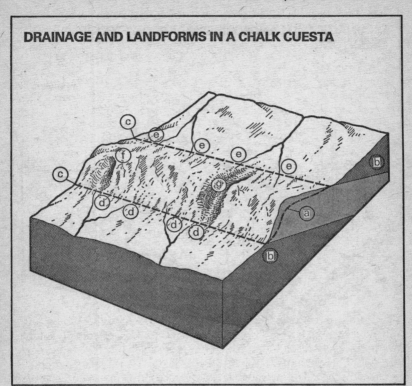

Your textbook probably gives a detailed treatment of this topic. Use it in making sure you can describe and explain the features lettered in this diagram, which should be compared with (B) on p31.

(a) **water table** or **level of saturation** within the chalk stratum. Level rises or falls according to the weather
(b) impervious clay stratum restricting downward seepage of water
(c) **spring line,** at which water table is at ground level, and where water flows out from fissures in the chalk
(d) **scarp-foot spring** which slowly erodes the impervious clay, thus undercutting chalk scarp and preserving its steep face
(e) **dip slope spring** cutting a valley on the 'back slope'
(f) **dry valley** and (g) **wind gap** (dry valley cutting right through scarp crest). Origins uncertain (*see opposite*) but occupied by streams which now rise at lower levels except when very wet weather raises the water table. Then, in some cases, **'winterbournes'** flow for a time from a higher spring line.

DRAINAGE AND LANDFORMS IN CARBONIFEROUS LIMESTONE

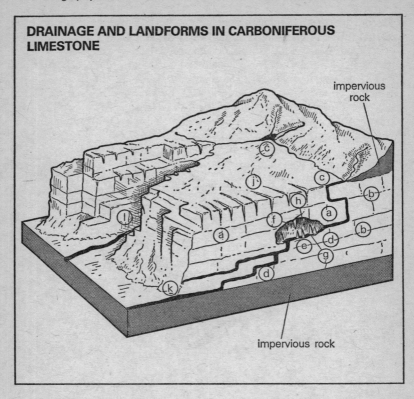

The main landforms associated with karst areas are lettered in this diagram and listed below. Make sure you understand their formation. Find in your textbook more details to add to the notes. Which four features would you name in answering part (c) of the question on p38 ?

- (a) **joints** and (b) **bedding planes** which developed as the limestone originally hardened and shrank
- (c) **swallow hole** or **sink** (or 'pot') formed by drainage of surface storm water
- (d) and (e) **underground stream and lake**
- (f) **cavern,** probably formed by scouring by sudden storm floods
- (g) **stalagmites** and (h) **stalactites,** very slowly formed by evaporation of lime-laden drips of water
- (j) **limestone pavement** with **clints** (slabs) and **grikes** (fissures)
- (k) **resurgent stream** emerging at level of impervious stratum underlying the limestone
- (l) **gorge** cut by stream now flowing underground ; steep-sided because of well-jointed rock formation (NB *contrast with chalk*).

Carboniferous limestone scenery Carboniferous limestone is much older and harder than chalk, and is not porous. The well-developed joint and bedding planes are, however, widened by water passing through and dissolving them, so that it is an extremely pervious formation with very few surface streams.

Soil is thin or completely absent, and vegetation rather sparse. Heavy rain, therefore, passes quickly underground and floods through fissures and crevices, widening them into the shafts and galleries in which pot-holders practise their dangerous sport. The result is a very distinctive landscape called **karst** (from its occurence in the Karst region of Yugoslavia). In England it is found in the Mendips, the northern Pennines and the Peak District of Derbyshire.

Underground water supplies Various permeable rocks, in particular chalk and sandstone, are locally important as **aquifers** – water-bearing strata. Boreholes are sunk to great depths to reach these rocks, from which comes the water supply for millions of people in Britain alone. A special type of aquifer is illustrated in the diagrams. Note that the artesian effect depends on its being 'sandwiched' between impervious strata.

Much of London's water comes in this way from the chalk syncline which underlies Greater London; but the rate of extraction exceeds the rate of natural replenishment, and the water table has fallen so far that pumping is necessary.

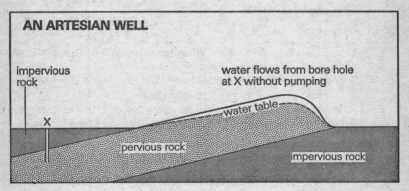

Locate the water table in this diagram. At what point would you expect to find natural springs? Why does water flow from a borehole sunk at X? Why does it not reach the surface without a borehole? Why does it cease to flow if it is over-used?

The work of rivers Water is an effective agent of erosion long before it forms part of a stream. Even separate raindrops can cause grains of soil to move slowly downhill. In a heavy shower the water may stream over the ground in **rills,** removing surface material by **rain-wash.** Alternate soaking and drying causes **soil creep,** which over a long period moves huge quantities of weathered material downhill. Really prolonged rain can cause **landslides.**

Thus every hollow and valley tends to become infilled with rock waste removed from higher slopes. In the same way the water itself collects in the lower levels, and at some point forms a recognizable stream running in a defined channel. This stream often begins at a **spring** where underground water emerges, and in most cases it is soon swollen by **tributaries. Eroding** its bed and banks, it **transports** the resulting material as its **load** and ultimately **deposits** it in the sea. These three aspects of a river's activity are all covered by questions such as:

13 (a) (i) *State* four *processes of erosion by which a river obtains its load.*
(ii) *Describe how a river transports its load.* (iii) *When and where is the load deposited?*
(b) *With the aid of diagrams explain how a river may form:* (i) *a meander;* (ii) *a delta.* (CAM)

From the following notes you will be able to work out an outline; to write a full answer you will need to add more details from a good physical geography textbook.

(a) (i) *River obtains load* by

1 **hydraulic action** – force of water removes loose material and weakens exposed surfaces;
2 **corrasion** – moving stones banged and rubbed against beds and banks, grind away more material;
3 **attrition** – material broken smaller while in transport;
4 **solution** – limestone and other rocks dissolved by water.

(ii) *River transports load*

1 **in solution;**
2 **in suspension** – small particles forming up to $\frac{2}{3}$ of load;
3 **by saltation** – larger particles and small pebbles bounce along stream bed; in flood, stream moves large pebbles and even boulders.

(Note the particular importance of flood conditions. Deeper water flows faster, because less of the stream is retarded by friction against banks and bed. If a stream's velocity is doubled it can carry particles sixty-four times heavier. This explains the damage caused by rivers in flood, and also the fact that very large boulders are found in the beds of streams which are normally quite small.)

(iii) It follows that *a river deposits its load* when it can no longer carry it, eg:

    1 when dry weather reduces the volume of water, or
    2 when the velocity slackens as the river enters a lake or a section of its course where the gradient is less steep.

For any given volume and velocity there is a maximum load, and something must be dropped if more is to be picked up. The result is seen, eg on bends where material is being deposited on the inside edge and at the same time removed from the outside edge, where the current runs faster.

(b) *Meanders and deltas:*
both topics are fully covered in most physical geography textbooks. Make sure you understand them and can draw the diagrams required, including meander cross-sections.

NB 1 You are asked 'How ?' and not 'Why ?' The reasons for the formation of meanders are not fully understood.

    2 Deltas are normal, not unusual, deposition features. It is only where the **estuary** is kept clear by strong tidal currents (eg the Mersey) or where, as in most British rivers, a rise in sea level (p55) has 'drowned' the lower course, that deltas are not found.

River development   The following questions deal with the development of a river system rather than with the process of erosion. **River capture** in particular is a frequent question-topic.

14 With the aid of annotated sketch-maps and/or diagrams describe the appearance of, and processes responsible for, the formation of features associated with river capture.   (LOND)

15 With the aid of diagrams explain the development of a river system in an area of gently dipping sedimentary rocks.   (OX)

Study the diagrams overleaf and complete the following notes:

1 In diagram (a) the land surface has fairly recently emerged above sea level. Streams Y and Z have begun to drain directly to the sea, carving valleys down the dip slope.
2 In diagram (b) these have been joined, roughly at right angles, by tributaries cutting along the (*strike ?/dip ?*) of the (*more ?/less ?*)

RIVER DEVELOPMENT AND CAPTURE

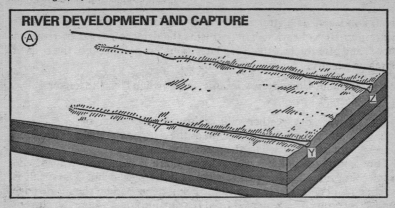

Ⓐ

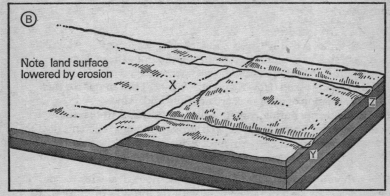

Ⓑ

Note land surface
lowered by erosion

X

Z

Y

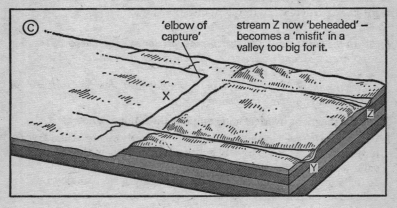

Ⓒ

'elbow of
capture'

stream Z now 'beheaded' –
becomes a 'misfit' in a
valley too big for it.

X

Z

Y

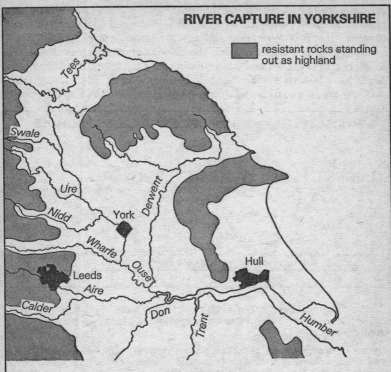

RIVER CAPTURE IN YORKSHIRE

▮ resistant rocks standing out as highland

The Yorkshire Ouse was originally a **strike stream**. It has cut back in the relatively soft rocks of what is now the Vale of York, capturing four **dip-slope streams** which almost certainly once flowed directly and separately into the sea.

resistant strata. The (*more ?/less ?*) resistant rocks are beginning to stand out as cuestas (p30). For some reason the (*dip slope ?/strike ?*) stream X is eroding its bed very actively and cutting (*back ?/forward ?*) towards stream Z.

3 In diagram (c) stream X has **captured** the waters of the (*upper ?/ lower ?*) course of stream Z, which now has (*less ?/more ?*) power to deepen its valley. Stream X now has (*more ?/less ?*) energy and so is (*less ?/more ?*) likely, in due course, to capture sections of other rivers.

Copy the diagrams and label them fully. Write full answers to the two questions.

River profiles   You may be questioned on the features typical of a river at different points in its course. It is important to remember – and to state – that no two rivers are alike, and that no river is 'typical'. Some rivers rise in coastal mountains and flow as short torrents to the sea. Some rise in lowlands and flow quietly along the whole of their course. Some have waterfalls close to their mouths. Nevertheless many rivers do show **cross-profiles** and a **long-profile** similar to those below.

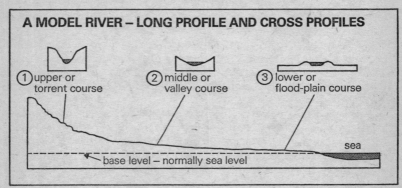

A MODEL RIVER – LONG PROFILE AND CROSS PROFILES

① upper or torrent course
② middle or valley course
③ lower or flood-plain course

sea

base level – normally sea level

Consider any rivers and streams you know at first hand, if possible with the help of OS maps, and identify as many as possible of the features listed in these notes:

Upper course   Gradient steep overall, but irregular, with many waterfalls and pools; volume very variable (depending on local rainfall); corrasion by boulders at flood periods causes rapid vertical erosion; valley thus narrow and deep; stream easily diverted, so valley winds between **interlocking spurs** of high ground.

Middle course   Gradient less steep, but incoming tributaries give greater volume and therefore greater erosive energy; **lateral erosion** increasingly effective, making valley wider and (relatively) shallower by cutting back spurs to form river cliffs; heavy load carried.

Lower course   Near sea level, so vertical erosion very slight, and energy used in lateral erosion; valley therefore wide and level; load now at maximum, so further transport possible only after dropping part of existing load; slight rise in water level causes overflows across the **flood plain**; on leaving main channel and slowing down, flood waters drop much of their load, forming natural banks (**levées**) between which the river drops more **alluvium**, so raising its bed above flood plain level. Rest of load finally dropped on entering sea, so river builds its delta further and further seaward, thus forming an alluvial coastal plain.

NB The three stages are not necessarily equal in length – these are diagrams, not scale models.

Erosion, transport and deposition by moving ice

The essential feature of ice erosion is its intensity. Ice does not move until it attains a certain thickness. When it does move, it moves very slowly. Subsequent snow adds a still greater depth. Added depth means added weight. Ice, moreover, seizes and holds firm the rock fragments it picks up, and scrapes them over the underlying surface, leaving tell-tale scratch marks called **striations** – a sure sign of ice erosion. Since the deepest hollows have the greatest weight of ice above them they are cut deeper still, so that the gradient of a glacial valley is very uneven. This **overdeepening** is illustrated below.

Compare diagram (A) with 1 opposite. A change in the climate has brought lower temperatures and a **valley glacier** has formed. Its great weight enables it to erode the land surface much faster and straighter than the former stream. Erosion is slower in the side valleys where the ice is not so deep.

Diagram (B) shows the landforms revealed when the climate improves and the ice melts. The stream now runs in a much deeper valley. Tributaries join it by way of waterfalls from **hanging valleys**. **Truncated (cut-off) spurs** contrast with the interlocking spurs of stream erosion, giving a typically deep, straight, U-shaped appearance as compared with the previous V-shape. The 'U' is partly masked by **moraine** and **scree** (*see overleaf and p35*) along the floor and lower sides of the valley.

Questions on glaciation are almost always about the resulting landforms, and often require the candidate to interpret a photograph of a glaciated highland area. You should therefore find and study such

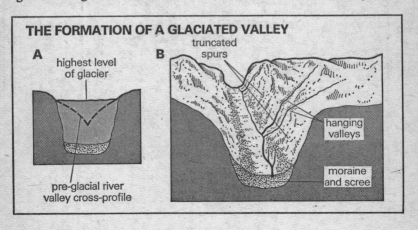

THE FORMATION OF A GLACIATED VALLEY

A

highest level
of glacier

pre-glacial river
valley cross-profile

B

truncated
spurs

hanging
valleys

moraine
and scree

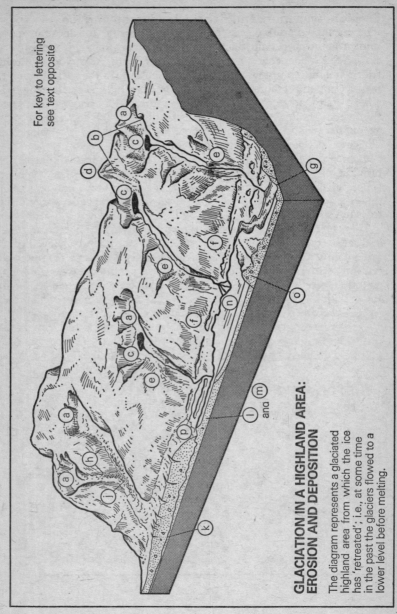

For key to lettering
see text opposite

GLACIATION IN A HIGHLAND AREA: EROSION AND DEPOSITION

The diagram represents a glaciated highland area from which the ice has 'retreated'; i.e., at some time in the past the glaciers flowed to a lower level before melting.

photographs. Here is a typically-worded question you must be able to answer with reference to *every* glacial landform mentioned here.

*16 With the aid of annotated sketch-maps and/or diagrams, describe the
appearance of, and processes responsible for the formation of, corries
and hanging valleys.*   (LOND)

Note the importance of annotated sketch-maps and diagrams, and the request not merely for a description but also for an explanation. Use your textbook to amplify the outline given here.

Distinguish carefully the results of erosion from those of deposition. The diagram represents a highland area from which the ice is 'retreating'; that is, the climate is improving, the snow-line is higher than before and glaciers melt at a higher level.

The letters on the map on p48 represent:

1 *Erosion landforms*
(a) **corrie, cirque** or **cwm** (see overleaf);
(b) **arête,** formed when two corries overlap, eg Striding Edge on Helvellyn and Crib Goch on Snowdon;
(c) **basin lake** in a corrie (or elsewhere along an over-deepened valley floor) eg Red Tarn on Helvellyn;
(d) **pyramidal peak** where three or more corries overlap at the summit, eg Snowdon and the Matterhorn;
(e) **hanging valleys** and (f) **truncated spurs** (previous page);
(g) U-shaped main valley – seen here in long profile.

2 *Deposition landforms*
(h) **lateral moraine** – weathered rock fragments falling from the valley sides on to the ice;
(j) **medial moraine** – formed where two glaciers join;
(k **ground moraine** – material eroded and transported by the glacier itself;
(l) **end** (or **terminal**) **moraine** – material transported so far by the glacier, but too heavy for the stream of **melt-water** to move any further;
(m) **erratics** – boulders or pebbles of rock which are different from the bedrock of the place where they now lie, and which can only have been brought there by ice;
(n) **ribbon** or **finger** lakes (eg Loch Ness, Windermere) formed, in this diagram, by a dam of **recessional moraine** – end moraine marking the earlier position of the glacier **snout**. Similar lakes may result from overdeepening of the valley floor, eg where two glaciers met thus increasing the weight of ice in that part of the valley.

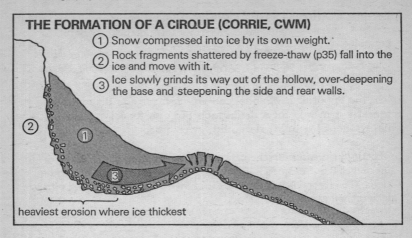

THE FORMATION OF A CIRQUE (CORRIE, CWM)

1. Snow compressed into ice by its own weight.
2. Rock fragments shattered by freeze-thaw (p35) fall into the ice and move with it.
3. Ice slowly grinds its way out of the hollow, over-deepening the base and steepening the side and rear walls.

heaviest erosion where ice thickest

If the climate is cold enough the mountain glaciers may flow out on to the adjacent lowlands and combine to form an **ice sheet**. When this melts it leaves behind a varied covering of **drift**. This may be in the form of **boulder clay** (or **till**) – particles of rock which have been ground very fine while being transported, and are then deposited over the countryside. Boulder clay contains large and small erratics, also from the melted ice, and this distinguishes it from ordinary clay. It is particularly important in eastern England, where it forms fertile soil. Other forms of till are the **outwash sands and gravels** – terminal moraine spread by floods of **melt-water** over a wide area; these are usually infertile, as in the Breckland of Norfolk.

Drumlins are oval hillocks of boulder clay, especially common in central Ireland. **Eskers** are long ridges of moraine, probably laid down in the bed of streams flowing under a glacier.

Glacial erosion mainly affects highlands, which it leaves stripped, gaunt and barren. Glacial deposition mainly affects lowlands. Nevertheless it pays to read questions carefully, as, for instance:

17 Choose a lowland region which has been subjected to glacial activity and explain how its main surface features were produced.   (ox)

You are asked to choose a (particular) lowland region, and the one you choose (eg East Anglia) may not show much surface evidence of erosion; but the question allows for erosion as well as for deposition, and in some lowlands glacial erosion has been very active (eg the lakes of Finland, most of them rock basins cut by an ice sheet).

Erosion, transport and deposition by wind

As an agent of transport, the wind is not very effective except in dry conditions. That is why this topic mainly concerns the landforms of hot and temperate deserts (p86).

Typical questions are:

18 Write an account, illustrated by examples, of [one *of four topics including*] *weathering and erosion in hot deserts.*   (LOND)

19 Describe and explain two *hot desert landforms,* one *formed by the wind and* one *due to the action of running water.*   (SUJB)

Mechanical weathering (p35) breaks rock down to very small fragments, but some experts consider that chemical weathering also plays a large part. The cold nights cause dew formation, and this moisture may help to promote further disintegration. Our essential starting point is the fact that the desert climate encourages the weathering of rock to fine particles (sand) which are light enough, in dry conditions, to blow with the wind.

The processes that follow desert weathering are:

1 **deflation** – the blowing away of finely weathered material, leaving surfaces bare for further weathering. Eddies in the wind may form hollows, though here, too, rock-rotting by moisture may enable the process to begin. The resulting hollow may be very large, eg the Qattara Depression in Egypt, whose floor is over 140m below sea level.

2 **abrasion** – the 'sand-blasting' and polishing of bare rock surfaces by blown sand, especially by the heavier particles blowing or bouncing near ground level. Rocks and slopes are undercut, and odd shapes occur where strata of different hardness alternate.

3 **attrition** – the sand grains are themselves polished and rounded by friction, producing great quantities of dust. Dust storms are a common hazard, and often reach the upper atmosphere. 'Red rain' caused by the washing down of Saharan dust has fallen as far away as Britain.

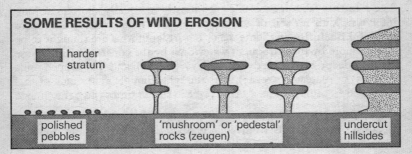

SOME RESULTS OF WIND EROSION

harder stratum

polished pebbles

'mushroom' or 'pedestal' rocks (zeugen)

undercut hillsides

THE FORMATION OF A BARKHAN

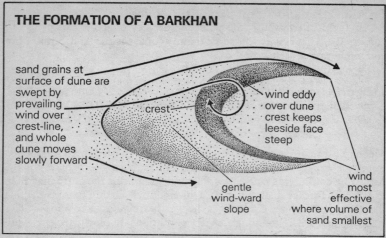

sand grains at surface of dune are swept by prevailing wind over crest-line, and whole dune moves slowly forward

crest

wind eddy over dune crest keeps leeside face steep

gentle wind-ward slope

wind most effective where volume of sand smallest

Desert landscapes   There are three main types:

1 **hamada** – bare rock, scoured clear of sand.
2 **reg** – a wind-scoured surface covered with sheets of pebbles cut into angular shapes. Little sand.
3 **erg** – sandy desert, with dunes as the typical landforms.

Most desert dunes are either:

1 **seif dunes** – steep-sided ridges up to 90m high and 90km long, lying parallel to the prevailing wind; *or*
2 **barkhans** – varying in height up to 30m and in width up to 350m. The diagram shows the reason for their typical crescent shape. Barkhans move slowly forward, growing, diminishing and changing in shape according to conditions.

The rain that falls in deserts comes mostly in squally showers at long intervals. With no soil or vegetation to soak it up, water runs off in powerful **flash floods**. Some major desert landforms are thought to be shaped more by the infrequent water than by the constant wind. These include deep, steep-sided dry valleys (**wadis**) and flat-topped hills (**buttes**) or plateaus (**mesas**). It is thought, though, that much of this large-scale erosion may have taken place in earlier times when the climate was wetter.

Collect more details from your textbooks and answer the previous two questions, using labelled diagrams.

LANDFORMS OF COASTAL EROSION

④ **stack** once part of the mainland, often formed by collapse of an arch

① **cliff face** where waves have cut back the coastline.

⑤ **stump** – a worn-down stack

② **cave** where a line of weakness in the cliff has been eroded

③ **arch**, cutting right through a mass of rock

⑥ beach material of rock, pebbles and sand, lying on:

⑦ **wave-cut bench** (or **marine platform**) levelled by erosion

Coastal erosion and deposition

20 *Give an illustrated account of the work of the sea in straightening an indented coastline.*   (LOND)

This half-question covers almost all of the ground normally tested at O level. The most frequent topics are (a) how the sea erodes the coastline, and (b) with what results. The latter are summarized in the diagram. If read in numbered order, the different landforms suggest how the process of erosion develops in a coastline of hard, resistant rocks.

The speed of coastal erosion naturally depends on the nature and structure of the rocks. It is carried out almost entirely by wave action, and in four ways:

1 **hydraulic action** of the tremendous pressure of breaking waves, reinforced by the **pneumatic** (blasting) **action** of air compressed into joint and cracks in the exposed rock surface;

2 **corrasion** by broken fragments battering the rock surface;

3 **attrition** as the fragments break and grind and smooth each other smaller and smaller, into pebbles, shingle and finally sand;

4 **chemical action** of the sea water on some rocks, dissolving or rotting the minerals of which the rocks are formed.

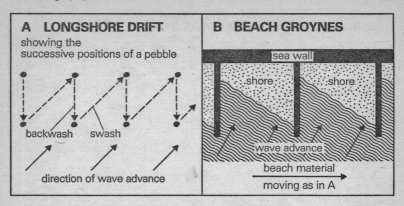

A LONGSHORE DRIFT
showing the
successive positions of a pebble

backwash   swash

direction of wave advance

B BEACH GROYNES

sea wall

shore   shore

wave advance

beach material
moving as in A

Waves have a **constructive** as well as a **destructive** role. Assisted by currents, they transport eroded material into sheltered waters where it forms (eg) **bayhead beaches** and **offshore bars,** features of a **coastline accretion.**

Where waves strike the coast obliquely, their successive **swash** and **backwash** carry sand and pebbles along the coast by **longshore drift** as in (A). To retain their beach, or rather to slow down its rate of removal, many seaside towns build groynes as in (B), against one side of which the beach material piles up.

Longshore drift often builds spits of sand and/or shingle across bays or river mouths, eg at Great Yarmouth, where the River Yare is diverted 4km southwards. Where a spit completely closes the inlet it forms a bar, as in (C). Thus, by cutting back the headlands and by filling in or cutting off the inlets, the sea tends to straighten an indented coastline.

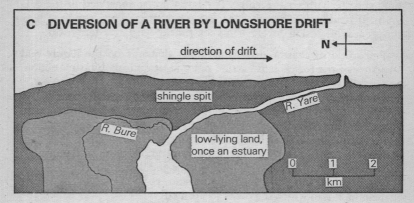

C DIVERSION OF A RIVER BY LONGSHORE DRIFT

direction of drift

N

shingle spit

R. Yare

R. Bure

low-lying land,
once an estuary

0   1   2
km

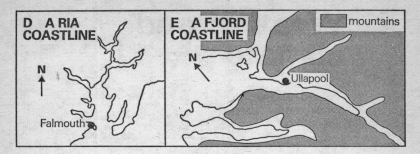

Changes of sea level

21 Describe the nature and results of changes in sea level. (LOND)

The form of a coastline often shows that sea level was once higher or lower. In the Western Highlands of Scotland there are wave-cut platforms behind and well above the present shore-line, covered with pebbles (now buried in soil and vegetation) and backed by cliffs which are no longer attacked by the highest waves. These **raised beaches** suggest that here the land stands above its former level. It is a **coast of emergence**. Such coasts develop for special local reasons.

Coasts of submergence, where the sea level has risen since the present land surface was first eroded, are more common. This is because the end of the last Ice Age released enormous quantities of melt-water into the oceans. Diagrams (D), (E) and (F) illustrate three types of 'drowned coast' which candidates are often asked to describe. The essential point to remember is that the rising waters have flooded into areas which were eroded as dry land.

You may be asked to distinguish between **concordant** and **discordant** coastlines. (F) is an example of a concordant coastline, where the 'grain' of the relief is parallel with the coast. In (D) and (E) the hills and valleys are roughly at right-angles to the coast and are thus discordant.

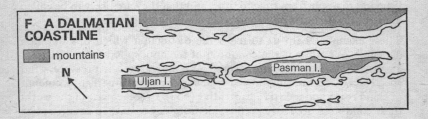

4 Weather and climate

22 '*Climate we take for granted; it's the weather that bothers us.*'
Distinguish between 'weather' and 'climate' (6 marks) *and discuss the
statement from the standpoint of (a) a farmer and (b) a heating
engineer* (7 marks each). (ox)

This question is worded unusually, but the suggested 'standpoints'
stimulate our ideas about the distinction between weather and climate.
Thoughts might run, with more detailed examples and references,
somewhat on the following lines:

Farmers live and work in almost every type of climate, and their plans
for each year are geared to their expectations of what will be possible.
A cotton grower will not suddenly decide to grow wheat, for he knows
the local *climate* is unsuitable; but having sown his cotton for the year,
he can only hope that the *weather* will be kind. Too much or too little
rain at the wrong time, or unduly strong winds, or unseasonably low
temperatures, are weather hazards which may spoil his plans.

Heating engineers can make a living only in regions where heating is
needed for at least part of the year. Their main task is to install equipment that will maintain a satisfactory level of temperature throughout
the coldest weather normally expected in that *climate*. To provide for
really exceptional 'cold snaps' will probably cost more than their customers care to pay. Nevertheless they know that unusually cold *weather*
is bound to occur from time to time, and that they are likely to be called
out to deal with burst pipes and other similar emergencies.

These examples help us to make the distinction which this question
demands. **Weather** is the condition of the atmosphere in one place at
a particular time, taking into account air temperature and pressure, wind
speed and direction, amount and type of **precipitation** (if any), amount
of cloud cover and **relative humidity** (p63). In some parts of the world
these conditions are fairly predictable from day to day. In countries like

Britain the weather often changes from hour to hour; yet certain weather conditions are recognized even here as typical of one time of year rather than another. These conditions, as the question says, we 'take for granted' and it is this 'average weather' for each season that makes up the **climate** of a given region.

Animal and vegetable life depends not only on sunlight but also on the **atmosphere**. This layer of mixed gases protects the Earth's surface from the lethal effects of unscreened radiation from the sun, and also 'blankets' it by slowing down the loss of heat from land and water surfaces after sunset. The atmosphere is perhaps 300km deep, but is so compressed by its own weight that well over half of it lies in the lower 10km. In this thin layer occur most of the events which determine our weather.

Weather observations

Direct questions on this topic are rare, but are usually very simple to anyone who has had the opportunity to handle the instruments and make observations. If you have had this experience, and if such questions regularly appear in the particular examination for which you are preparing, then use the following as a check list for revision:

1 **aneroid** and **mercury barometers** for registering atmospheric pressure;
2 **rain gauge** (*watch the spelling*) for registering total precipitation of all forms in the previous 24 hours;
3 **wind vane** for registering wind direction;
4 **anemometer** for registering wind speed;
5 **Campbell-Stokes sunshine recorder**;
6 **Stevenson screen** containing:
   (i) **wet and dry bulb thermometers** for registering air temperature and relative humidity;
   (ii) **maximum and minimum thermometers** for recording the maximum and minimum temperatures of the previous 24 hours.

In each of these cases you must be able to show the construction with a simple labelled diagram; describe the method of use; state special siting requirements; and explain the method of recording.

Questions on this topic are always at this simple. descriptive level.

The elements of weather

At any moment some parts of the atmosphere differ markedly from the surrounding air in their **temperature** and/or **pressure** and/or **humidity**. Even though these bodies of air may be moving, their differences often persist surprisingly long. In recent years the term **air mass** has come into common use because research has increasingly shown that 'weather' is what happens within these air masses or along the boundaries, often marked by abrupt change, between them.

The most frequently examined topic is the Daily Weather Map of Britain. See *Book 2* p25. The following other typical questions are covered in essential outline in this chapter or in *Book 2* Ch 1, but wider reading is very necessary.

23 *Condensation may occur with a fall in temperature.*
   (a) *(i) What is condensation? (ii) How is the cooling brought about?
     (iii) At what stage does the cooling cause condensation?*
   (b) *(i) Explain fully how clouds are formed. (ii) Describe two of the
     following types of cloud:* cirrus, stratus, cumulus, cumulo-nimbus.
   (c) *Name one type of precipitation which is formed when the
     temperature is below 0°C, and explain how it is caused.* (CAM)

24 *Answer two of the following:*
   (a) *What factors regulate air temperature near the surface of the Earth?
     Explain their seasonal variation.* (OX)
   (b) *(Similar to (1)(b) above.)* (OX)
   (c) *What is meant by relative humidity? How, and with what
     instruments, is it measured?*

25 *(i) Explain briefly how fogs are formed. (ii) Explain why cold air often accumulates in valley bottoms and show, with reference to one example, how this affects agriculture.* (SUJB)

26 *Choose two of the following types of weather and, by reference to a named region in each case, describe the meteorological conditions which give rise to them:
(i) Winds exceeding 30 knots (ii) Prolonged periods of sunshine (iii) Fog (iv) Thunderstorms (v) Abnormally low temperatures.
Illustrate your answers with sketch-maps and diagrams.* (LOND)

27 *(i) By means of sketches show the difference between stratus and cumulus clouds. (ii) Which of the two cloud formations would indicate favourable conditions for gliding? Why?* (SCOT)

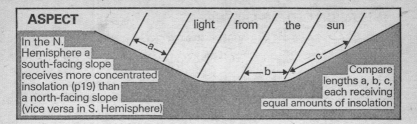

ASPECT   light from the sun

In the N. Hemisphere a south-facing slope receives more concentrated insolation (p19) than a north-facing slope (vice versa in S. Hemisphere)

Compare lengths a, b, c, each receiving equal amounts of insolation

Temperature

The atmosphere is warmed *indirectly* by the sun. Indirectly, because (i) sunlight passes through air without much effect, (ii) it strikes the Earth and warms its surface, (iii) the heat thus generated radiates back into the lower atmosphere, which it warms. The degree of warmth depends on several factors:

1 **latitude**   As shown on p19, the sun's radiation may reach the Earth in concentrated or in diffused form.
2 **altitude**   Air is less dense at higher altitudes, and usually contains less dust and less moisture. For all three reasons it is less able to retain heat radiated from the Earth's surface. The **lapse rate** (fall in temperature) with increased altitude is about 1°C per 150m in calm conditions. Mean temperatures in January at the summit of Ben Nevis (1343m) are about 8°C below those at its foot. To construct **isotherms** (lines joining points of equal temperature) for weather maps, the 'actual temperatures' for each weather station are therefore '**reduced to sea level**', ie *increased*, in proportion to the station's altitude.
3 **distance from the sea**   Because it gains and loses heat more slowly than land, the sea has a moderating influence on the climate of coastal areas, except where the prevailing wind (p67) is offshore. Coastal areas thus tend to have **equable** climates (a narrow range of temperature) whereas places far inland have **extreme** climates (a wide range of temperature).
4 **aspect** (see diagram).
5 **cloud, smoke or dust,** where they occur, shade the ground and reflect much of the sun's radiation back into space; but they also 'blanket' the Earth's surface and reduce the heat loss that in clearer conditions takes place at night.
6 **ocean currents** (see pp72–3).
NB   The effectiveness of factors 1, 3 and 4 vary, as shown on p19, with seasonal changes in the sun's altitude.

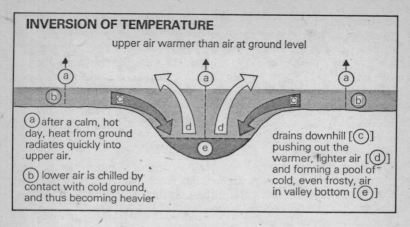

INVERSION OF TEMPERATURE

upper air warmer than air at ground level

(a) after a calm, hot day, heat from ground radiates quickly into upper air.

(b) lower air is chilled by contact with cold ground, and thus becoming heavier

drains downhill [(c)] pushing out the warmer, lighter air [(d)] and forming a pool of cold, even frosty, air in valley bottom [(e)]

Weather stations record **diurnal** (daily) **maximum** and **minimum temperatures**. Figures for each month, repeated over a long period (usually thirty years) are averaged to give **mean monthly temperatures** such as those quoted on pp77–83. The difference between means of the coldest and hottest months is the **mean annual range of temperature**. The **mean diurnal range** (the average day-to-night change) is also calculated, and in many parts of the world is wider than the annual range.

The normal lapse of temperature with increased altitude is sometimes affected by freak conditions which develop in the calm, still air of anti-cyclonic weather (p62). The result is an inversion of temperature; up to a certain altitude the temperature rises, instead of falling, as shown in this diagram.

The diagram answers Q25(ii) on p58 and explains why fruit farmers in particular avoid 'frost hollows' in which blossom may be nipped by unseasonable frosts. Thus, for example, in the Vale of Evesham (Worcs) and the Annapolis Valley (Nova Scotia, Canada) fruit trees are planted on the lower hill slopes rather than on the valley floor.

Another form of temperature inversion occurs in winter, when the air near ground level often becomes colder than the air at some distance above it. Moisture in the warmer layer then condenses to form a layer of cloud which the weak winter sunlight cannot penetrate. The result is 'anticyclonic gloom' – very dull weather, lasting until dispersed by a change of pressure conditions. Industrial smoke or traffic fumes may be trapped in the inversion layer and turn the cloud into **smog**.

Pressure

Air pressure varies (a) with altitude and (b) with changes of temperature. Warm air expands, so that a given space contains a lesser weight of warm air than of cold. Heavy (dense) air spreads out to displace warm, light air. This movement is felt as **wind**. It may occur on a world scale (the **planetary wind system**, p66) or on a purely local scale. In either case, winds affect the weather by 'importing' the temperature and moisture conditions of some other part of the Earth's surface.

Millibars (mb) are the units of measurement of atmospheric pressure. One bar (1000mb) is approximately the average air pressure at sea level.

Isobars are lines on maps joining points of equal pressure. Pressure readings for stations at different altitudes are 'reduced to sea level', ie increased, to compensate for the lower pressure of the air at higher altitudes. Just as contours close together indicate a steep slope on the ground, so isobars close together indicate a steep **pressure gradient,** ie a marked difference of pressure within a short distance. These are the conditions that give rise to strong local winds (Q26(i), p58).

One common example of a local wind is illustrated overleaf, and two others on p63. Diagram (B) relates to what is normally a gentle night breeze in a hot climate. The same diagram can be used to explain a winter wind such as the **mistral** of southern France. In the latter case, cold air collects over the snow-covered mountains inland. From time to time, when low pressure air lies over the nearby Mediterranean, the cold heavy air simply slides downhill under its own weight, like an avalanche, and is felt on the coast as a violent and persistent northerly gale. Draw the outline of diagram (B) and label it to illustrate the cause of the mistral as described here.

(*Note* Diagrams A and B if viewed on a continental (not local) scale and on a seasonal (not daily) basis, help to explain the cause of the monsoons of SE Asia and N Australia (pp69, 86).)

Other well-known local winds are:

1 the cold **bora** of the Adriatic coast of Yugoslavia;
2 the hot, dry **harmattan** of West Africa;
3 the hot, humid **sirocco** of southern Italy;
4 the hot, dry **khamsin** of Egypt;
5 the cold **etesian winds** of the Greek islands;
6 the cold **helm wind** of the northern Pennines (Eden Valley) – and of course the **cyclones, hurricanes** and **typhoons** which occur mainly in tropical regions.

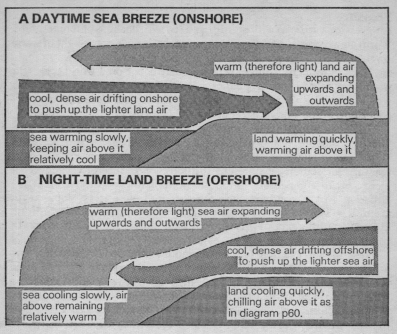

A DAYTIME SEA BREEZE (ONSHORE)

warm (therefore light) land air expanding upwards and outwards

cool, dense air drifting onshore to push up the lighter land air

sea warming slowly, keeping air above it relatively cool

land warming quickly, warming air above it

B NIGHT-TIME LAND BREEZE (OFFSHORE)

warm (therefore light) sea air expanding upwards and outwards

cool, dense air drifting offshore to push up the lighter sea air

sea cooling slowly, air above remaining relatively warm

land cooling quickly, chilling air above it as in diagram p60.

Land surfaces warm up and also cool down more quickly than water surfaces, because water absorbs heat to a greater depth than soil or rock. On a local and on a world scale, climate is greatly affected by this fact. These diagrams illustrate weather events that are very frequent in coastal areas during hot weather.

Warning: You must avoid using phrases which suggest that cool air is 'drawn in' because warm air rises or has risen. Notice in these diagrams that the cooler air *pushes* underneath the warmer air. This is the only reason why 'warm air rises'.

Sometimes a mass of high-pressure air (**anticyclone**, *Book 2* p18) lies over an area, producing calm or gently outblowing air in which the weather conditions of Q26(iv) or (v) may be expected. With no wind to bring in clouds, the sun will shine all day and a temporary 'heat wave' may develop during (eg) an English summer; though such conditions are typical, for months at a time, of (eg) the Sahara Desert in winter.

In an English winter, by contrast, the ground loses heat in the clear air of anticyclonic conditions, and temperatures may fall far below the average; but such weather is even more typical of winter in the centre of a landmass such as Siberia.

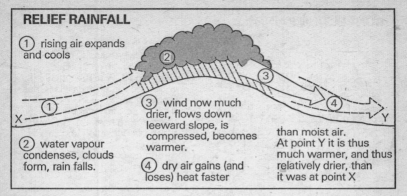

RELIEF RAINFALL

① rising air expands and cools

②

③

② water vapour condenses, clouds form, rain falls.

③ wind now much drier, flows down leeward slope, is compressed, becomes warmer.

④ dry air gains (and loses) heat faster

④ than moist air. At point Y it is thus much warmer, and thus relatively drier, than it was at point X

X — — —   — — — Y

Windward slopes often have a heavy rainfall, with a corresponding **rain shadow** effect to leeward. Compare the rainfall of the west and east coasts of Britain (*atlas map*).
Warning — avoid use of the word 'sheltered' in explaining this contrast. The low rainfall is the result of physical changes noted in the diagram.

For striking contrasts of temperature as well as of rainfall, see text-book descriptions of the **Föhn** and **Chinook** winds. On either of these, prepare to answer questions such as:

28 *Explain why* [this wind] *occurs, what its characteristics are, and the effect it has on man and his crops.*   (SCOT)

Humidity

The atmosphere contains huge amounts of water, either in liquid form or as an invisible gas (**water vapour**). When air contains as much water vapour as it can absorb, it is said to be **saturated**. Cold air cannot hold as much water vapour as warm air. Thus, without any increase in the **absolute humidity** (the actual water content) air becomes *relatively* wetter if it is cooled. **Relative humidity,** therefore, is the amount of moisture held by a body of air, expressed as a percentage of the maximum it could hold *at that temperature.*

Condensation is the change from gaseous to liquid form which takes place when the relative humidity reaches 100 per cent (ie when the air becomes saturated). This level of saturation – varying with temperature – is called **dew-point**. At dew-point some of the water vapour condenses into droplets which hang in the air (**cloud**) or at ground level (**fog and mist**) or collect on cold objects (**dew**).

NB condensation requires not only a fall in temperature but also a nucleus, such as a particle of dust, salt or smoke, for each droplet.

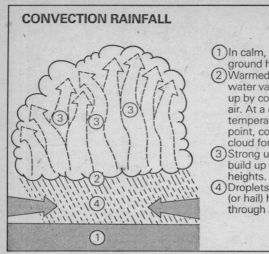

CONVECTION RAINFALL

1. In calm, warm conditions hot ground heats overlying air.
2. Warmed air, with its contained water vapour, rises as it is forced up by cooler, denser inflowing air. At a certain level the air temperature has fallen to dew point, condensation begins and cloud forms.
3. Strong up-currents (**thermals**) build up the cloud to great heights.
4. Droplets merge into large drops (or hail) heavy enough to fall through ascending air currents.

Air may be cooled to dew-point in several ways:

1 by radiation on a calm, clear night (diagram p60);
2 by the passage of warm air over cold ground;
3 by contact between cold and warm air masses, p72;
4 by ascent, as in the diagrams above and on p63. This is much the most important form of condensation. Rising air expands because the air pressure is decreasing (p61). Expansion causes cooling, just as compression causes heating (eg as in a cycle pump). Conversely, descending air grows drier (ie its relative humidity and dew-point fall) as its temperature rises; so that clouds and other forms of visible moisture evaporate and the sky clears.

Precipitation

Droplets of water, once condensed, may remain suspended in the air or may combine into heavier drops which fall to earth in various forms:

1 **rain** is of three types:
  (i) **relief** or **orographic rainfall** (diagram, p63);
  (ii) **frontal** or **depression rainfall** (*Book 2* pp15, 18–21);
  (iii) **convection rainfall** (diagram above);
2 **hail** consists of ice pellets formed in conditions of very strong convection and are thus typically associated with thunderstorms;
3 **snow** is formed when water vapour condenses directly into solid ice particles which combine into flakes;

4 **sleet** is falling snow which has partially melted;
5 **dew** forms when water vapour condenses directly on to cold ground surfaces; *but* –
6 **frost** forms instead of dew if the ground surfaces have cooled below freezing point.

Clouds   This topic is detailed and complicated, and only a brief outline can be given here.

The process of cloud formation was mentioned on p63. Clouds are of three basic types:

1 **cirrus** feathery, wispy, high-level, consisting of ice particles and formed by contact between air masses of slightly different temperatures. A fair-weather cloud.
2 **stratus** a thin, widespread sheet at low to medium height, formed by contact between two layers of air of different temperatures. In certain conditions (eg in the **warm front** of a **depression** – *Book 2* pp19–21) the stratus thickens to **nimbo-stratus,** with continuous drizzle or steady rain.
3 **cumulus** piled-up masses with flat bases (at dew-point level) resulting from rapid upward movement caused by relief (diagram p63) or convection. With continued upward movement **cumulo-nimbus** develops (diagram, opposite) and heavy rain falls, often as part of a thunderstorm.

All three types are illustrated on p21 of *Book 2*, but there are many variations and combinations of cloud shape, and to cover the topic fully a book containing good cloud photographs is required. Two such books are:

Forsdyke *The Weather Guide* (Hamlyn).

E. W. Young *Weather in Britain, Basic Studies S3* (Edward Arnold).

Fog and **mist** (thin fog) are caused:
1 by radiation in calm air (diagram p60);
2 by **advection** – the passage of moist air over a cold (land or sea) surface. Very common along 'cold water coasts' (p72).

Study in turn each of the diagrams in this chapter so far, then put the book aside and explain in your own words the point each diagram illustrates. Check your answer against the captions and accompanying text.

Outline an answer to each of the questions on p58. Note that each calls for a number of short answers; most of them need the help of diagrams even if not specifically demanded.

The elements of climate

The elements of world climate are the same as those of local weather –
temperature, pressure and humidity. Questions on the principles of
climate are quite rare, and are generally limited to short points of fact;
but those principles underlie much that is common to all syllabuses, and
must therefore be clearly understood.

Typical questions and part-questions are:

29 *The world map* (supplied separately) *shows those areas which
experience mean annual precipitation totals of over 1500mm and less
than 250mm.*
  (*a*) (*i*) *Briefly explain how mean annual precipitation figures are
calculated;* (*ii*) *Briefly describe three* other *aspects of precipitation
information that the mean annual precipitation figures do not show.*
  (*b*) *Choose* one *area experiencing over 1500mm per annum and* one
*area experiencing under 250mm per annum and, in each case,
explain the factors responsible for the annual precipitation totals.
Credit will be given for any relevant information added to the
map.*   (LOND)

30 *The world map* (supplied separately) *shows the seasonal distribution
of rainfall. Choose three of the rainfall regimes shown and in each case,
with reference to a named area, explain the seasonal distribution.*
(JMB)

31 (*a*) *What is a prevailing wind ?*
  (*b*) *What are the general characteristics of the Trade Winds ?*
  (*c*) *Describe and explain the effect on the climate of coastal areas of
an onshore wind passing over a warm ocean current.*   (CAM)

32 (*a*) *On the world outline map* (supplied separately) *mark and name*
two *warm and two* cold *ocean currents.*
  (*b*) *Explain with the aid of diagrams how* one *of the warm currents and*
one *of the cold currents named in* (*a*) *have influenced the climate
of the neighbouring coastal regions.*   (LOND)

NB (i) 'Rainfall' may be assumed to include all forms of precipitation,
unless a more limited meaning is made clear in the question.
  (ii) Questions on ocean currents are almost always linked with
their effect on climate, and the topic is therefore included in
this chapter.

World pressure and wind systems – theoretical
Your textbook almost certainly contains a diagram illustrating the
planetary wind system. Can you draw it from memory, and do you

understand it? As a revision check, construct a labelled diagram covering the following points. When complete, compare it with your textbook.

1 The midday sun is always overhead somewhere between the Tropics. This accounts for the **Inter-tropical Convergence Zone (ITCZ)** of hot, and therefore expanding, light air; a region of calms and heavy convectional rainfall.

2 This air is forced upwards by denser air flowing in strongly and steadily from north and south – the NE and SE **Trade Winds.**

3 The displaced air flows away at a high level towards the Poles. Much of it goes no further than about 30°N and S, where it forms a dense, high-pressure air mass settling down to ground level. As it settles it grows warmer by compression and its relative humidity falls, so that rain is very rare.

4 From this subtropical high-pressure zone the ground level winds blow Equatorward (the Trade Winds) or Poleward.

5 Both the Equatorward and the Poleward flows are deflected by the Earth's rotation – to the right in the Northern Hemisphere, to the left in the Southern Hemisphere.

6 The Poles are covered by a very cold, dense air mass from which strong but variable winds blow outwards.

7 These winds meet and merge with those from the subtropical high-pressure around latitudes 50°–60°, at the **Polar Front**, where their differing temperatures give rise to very changeable weather (*Book 2* pp18–19). This is especially true in the Northern Hemisphere.

World pressure and wind systems – actual
There are thus two belts of Trade Winds, marked by their strength, steadiness and regularity; and two of **Westerlies**, much more variable in force and direction. Together they form the **prevailing winds** (ie those which blow most frequently from one specific direction) over most of the Earth.

This orderly pattern is affected by two factors:

1 The apparent migration of the overhead sun (p20) causes a seasonal swing of the 'heat equator' (the ITCZ) and of the other wind and pressure 'belts', which move north and south through about 10° of latitude.

2 Since land and water react differently to insolation (p62), the distribution of continents and oceans breaks the uniformity of the pressure 'belts' and produces drastic seasonal changes of wind direction.

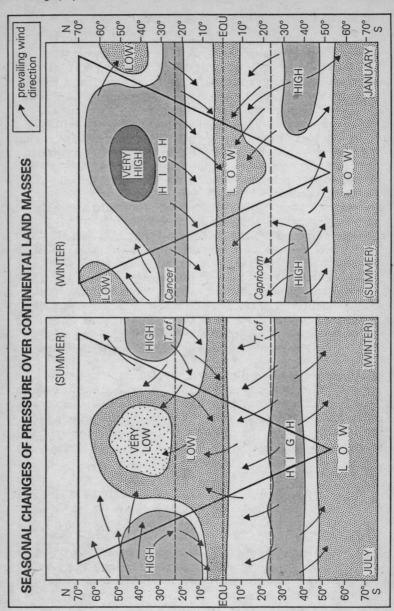

SEASONAL CHANGES OF PRESSURE OVER CONTINENTAL LAND MASSES

These diagrams illustrate the effect of factors 1 and 2 in the previous paragraph. Notice how the high and low pressure areas form contrasting 'cells' over land and sea rather than continuous east-west 'belts'. Compare each diagram with the maps of world temperature, pressure and rainfall in your atlas or textbook. Identify the following:

1 Equatorial regions of constant high temperature and low pressure, and of frequent heavy convectional rainfall.

2 North or south of 1, regions with similar conditions *in summer only*. In winter these regions experience the Trade Winds, with heavy rainfall on east coasts diminishing to low rainfall on west coasts.

3 In the northern continents, their broad extent east-west results in a land/sea contrast of temperature and pressure that breaks the planetary wind pattern. Thus, in summer, rain-bearing winds easily penetrate to the heart of the continent. In winter this is unusual, and precipitation totals (mainly in the form of snow) are low.

4 The Westerlies bring rain to the west coast:
   (a) in latitudes 40°–60°N all the year;
   (b) in latitudes 30°–40°N in winter, when the high-pressure belt has shifted south;
   (c) as in (a), and also to the continental interior, in summer (3 above).

5 The southern continents are too narrow to have much influence on the planetary pressure system, though over the interior pressure is sufficiently low in summer to allow inblowing winds which bring most of the year's rainfall (as in 2). Winters are dry except on the east coast. Between 30° and 40°S is a west coast rainfall/summer drought region corresponding to that in the northern continents.

This model can be related quite closely to the Americas, and fairly closely to Europe-with-Africa, except for complications arising from Europe's link with the land mass of Asia. Prevailing winds are indicated very approximately.

Redrawn with a wide break along the Equator, the model can be modified to apply to Asia-with-Australia. Construct and, using your atlas or textbook, add details of pressure and winds to such a pair of diagrams. These will show how the influence of land and sea partly reverses the planetary air flow and produces the winter and summer **monsoons** in both continents. Shade the areas of heavy rainfall in each season, and note how they are related to the seasonal reversal of wind direction.

This very brief summary covers most of the climatic types commonly tested, and it is absolutely essential to understand the temperature/pressure/rainfall relationships involved before going on to the more detailed work of the next chapter.

Rainfall in its various aspects

Used in connection with the climate of a particular place, the word 'rainfall' usually signifies its **total mean annual precipitation**. It is used in this sense in Chapter 5. The figure is arrived at by adding daily totals to establish totals for each month of the year. The monthly totals are averaged over a long period, as with temperature (p62), and totalled again to give a mean annual total.

If we know only this much about the climate of a place we can make shrewd guesses as to what activities we can expect to find there; yet the picture remains far from complete, even in respect of precipitation. We must ask also:

1 *What form* does the precipitation take? In the Canadian prairies the winter total is low, but since it all comes as snow, accumulating until the spring thaw, it is enough to give the newly-sown grain a good damp start to the growing season.
2 *How reliable* is it? Farmers have to guess what next season's weather will be like (p56). In many regions it seldom varies far from the mean. In the great rice- and wheat-growing lands on which most of the world's people depend for food, annual rainfall totals unfortunately vary quite widely.
3 *What form* does it take? Fairly frequent gentle showers are obviously preferable to occasional heavy storms. Unfortunately the regions of unreliable rainfall are often also those where violent convectional rain is the typical form of precipitation.
4 *When does it fall?* The map of **rainfall regimes** (*opposite*) sets out in very simplified form the **seasonal distribution of precipitation** throughout the world. Many places have (say) 1000mm mean annual total; but since some of these have summer drought, some have winter drought and some have no dry season, there are wide differences in the rhythm of their farming year.

You should now be able to write adequate answers to questions 29, 30 and 31(a) and (b) on p66; but to do better still, study the map opposite very thoroughly and relate it to the more detailed information in Chapter 5, from which you must be able to quote named examples and accurate figures (of temperature as well as rainfall) in answering questions of this type.

We have already seen that proximity to the sea increases the rainfall of many places. How, then, do we account for the odd fact that many of the world's driest deserts lie on the coast?

SEASONAL DISTRIBUTION OF RAINFALL

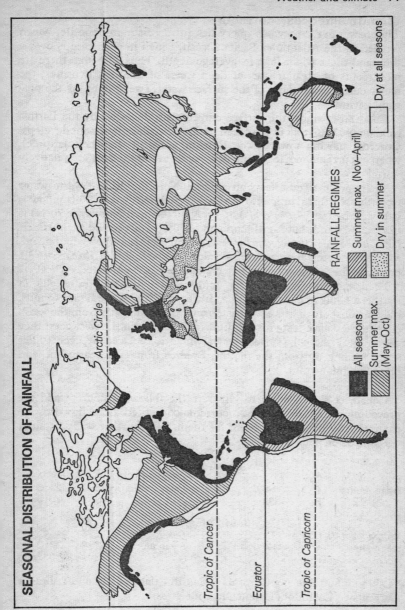

Arctic Circle

Tropic of Cancer

Equator

Tropic of Capricorn

RAINFALL REGIMES

All seasons

Summer max. (May–Oct)

Summer max. (Nov–April)

Dry in summer

Dry at all seasons

Climate and ocean currents

The answer to the previous query lies in the diagram opposite, which represents the Atlantic *or* Pacific Ocean, which in each case is over a thousand times wider than its average depth. Thus, although there are movements of great masses of deep water of different densities, the major currents are those of the surface water, swept along by the prevailing winds.

Like those winds, the surface currents are deflected by the Earth's rotation (p67), so that in the ocean basins a circular movement develops. Currents moving towards the Equator are cool (for their latitude), whereas currents moving along or away from the Equator are relatively warm.

There are marked effects on climate. Note the drift of warm water from the North Atlantic into the almost enclosed Arctic. This inflow is balanced by (*which two cold outflows ?*).* Northern Norway (*c* 70°N) is never ice-bound, but Newfoundland (*c* 50°N) is icebound each winter. (*Which two currents account for this contrast ?*)† Around Newfoundland, too, the mingling of warm and cold air from above (*which two currents ?*)‡ produces the frequent fogs which are a feature of the climate.

Even more striking are the **'cold water coasts'**, especially of northern Chile and South Africa. In these latitudes the Trade Winds, blowing onshore on the east coast, bring warm, moist air from the warm current they have just crossed. Blowing offshore on the west coast they sweep away the cold surface water which is replaced by even colder water welling up from the depths. Breezes from cold sea to hot land bring fog, but no rain.

Construct sketch-maps to illustrate the following figures; add the prevailing winds and the ocean currents concerned. State in words the contrasts you note, and account for them. After further study, attempt 3 and 32 on p66.

South Africa

Port Nolloth (29°S)			Durban (30°S)			
mean annual	T°	14°C	mean annual	T°	21°C	
,, ,,	R	60mm	,, ,,	R	1010mm	

South America

Antofagasta (24°S)			Rio de Janeiro (23°S)			
mean annual	T°	17°C	mean annual	T°	23°C	
,, ,,	R	13mm	,, ,,	R	1082mm	

*Labrador and Behring Currents †North Atlantic Drift and Labrador Currents ‡Labrador Current and Gulf Stream

PREVAILING WINDS AND OCEAN CURRENTS

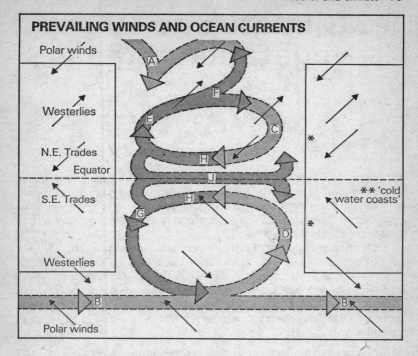

The letters correspond to the following currents in the Atlantic and Pacific Oceans (Atlantic currents stated first). Identify them on an atlas or textbook map of ocean currents. Draw a labelled world sketch-map, using red and blue arrows, and learn the position of each one.

Cold currents

(A) Labrador/Behring
(C) Canaries/Californian

(B) Antarctic *or* West Wind Drift
(D) Benguela/Peruvian (*or* Humboldt)

Warm currents

(E) Gulf Stream/Kuro Siwo
(G) Brazilian/(*in Indian Ocean*) Mozambique
(H) N and S Equatorial

(F) North Atlantic Drift/North Pacific Current
(J) Guinea/Equatorial Counter-current

Note The Indian Ocean does not conform exactly to this pattern, partly because of its restricted shape and partly because the seasonal reversal of the monsoon winds (p69) causes a reversal of the currents around the Indian coast.

5 Climate and vegetation regions

From the facts summarized in Chapter 4 it is clear that in any given place the climate depends on certain factors, some perhaps constant throughout the year, others changing seasonally. It is also clear that these factors have *more or less* similar effects in a place in a corresponding position in another continent.

Thus arises the concept of **climatic regions**, with a world map (*opposite*) neatly divided into a 'jigsaw' which corresponds fairly closely to that on p71, and which is summarized in the diagram overleaf. Maps and diagrams like this are very useful aids to memorizing the general pattern, and to understanding the similarities and differences of human response in widely separated parts of the world, but they must be used carefully since:

1 the apparent boundaries mark zones of transition and not lines of sudden change;
2 within each region there are many exceptions arising from local factors of altitude, aspect, etc.

Despite these reservations it is essential to know this map thoroughly, because almost all Boards regularly set questions on the topic of climate regions and on the types of vegetation and human activity associated with each one. Questions are of several types. Some are purely verbal, eg:

33 *Explain* three *of the following statements:*
    (*a*) *In the steppe lands the rainfall occurs mainly in summer and is low in amount;*
    (*b*) *The coastlands of South and East Asia experience seasonal changes in wind direction and heavy rainfall;*
    (*c*) (*d*) (Similar statements about other climate regions). (JMB)

Your answer to (*a*) has to show where the steppe lands are (with a named example and seasonal rainfall totals) and what factors give rise to the

D THE WORLD – CLIMATE REGIONS

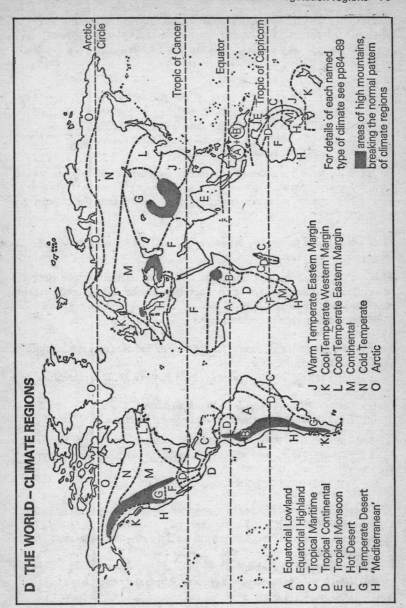

A Equatorial Lowland
B Equatorial Highland
C Tropical Maritime
D Tropical Continental
E Tropical Monsoon
F Hot Desert
G Temperate Desert
H 'Mediterranean'

J Warm Temperate Eastern Margin
K Cool Temperate Western Margin
L Cool Temperate Eastern Margin
M Continental
N Cold Temperate
O Arctic

For details of each named
type of climate see pp84–89

areas of high mountains,
breaking the normal pattern
of climate regions

Arctic
Circle

Tropic of Cancer

Equator

Tropic of Capricorn

features mentioned. *Simple, labelled* sketch-maps or diagrams showing summer and winter conditions, with a short explanatory paragraph, form the neatest way of dealing with three such statements concisely yet fully.

34 *Explain each of the following:*
   (a) *Some of the scattered trees of the tropical grassland have large (swollen) trunks and long roots, and they are umbrella-shaped;*
   (b) *The tundra has short-rooted plants and stunted bushes and there is an absence of trees;* (and similar statements about the vegetation of two other climate regions).   (CAM)

To 'explain' such a statement, state not only the conditions in which such vegetation grows but also the climatic factors involved. As this is only a half-question, there is time for no more than brief, orderly summaries as on pp84–9.

35 *What physical factors are associated with (a) tundra vegetation and (b) temperate grassland?*   (OX)

This was a full question, and thus called for a much more detailed description and *explanation* of the factors (climate and, to some extent, relief and soils) involved.

    Other questions are numerical, eg:

36 *Examine the following figures for stations A and B:* (two sets of figures similar to those on pp82–3)
   (a) *For* each station *describe the main feature of its temperature and rainfall;*
   (b) *Name the climate region in which each lies;*
   (c) *Explain the two temperature and rainfall patterns.*   (SUJB)

This is a simple question, requiring only a careful analysis of the figures (*as suggested overleaf*) and enough knowledge to identify the type of climate and explain its causes.

    You may be required to make use of fewer facts, eg:

37 *Four towns are marked on the accompanying world map and indicated by letters A,B,C,D. The January and July temperature and rainfall figures and the mean annual rainfall total for the four towns are labelled 1,2,3,4.*
   (Details set out as a table)
   (a) *State, with reasons, which of sets 1,2,3,4 refers to each of towns A,B,C,D.*

CLIMATE REGIONS – A SUMMARY MODEL

(after L. D. Stamp)

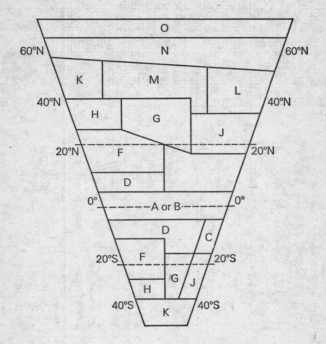

This diagram is lettered as in the previous map. It is a valuable revision device if used as a test of memory of the features of each type of climate as set out in this chapter; and, even more important, of the reasons for those features, as explained by the location of the region within the land mass as a whole.

A copy of the diagram could usefully be shaded to show the rainfall regimes (p71).

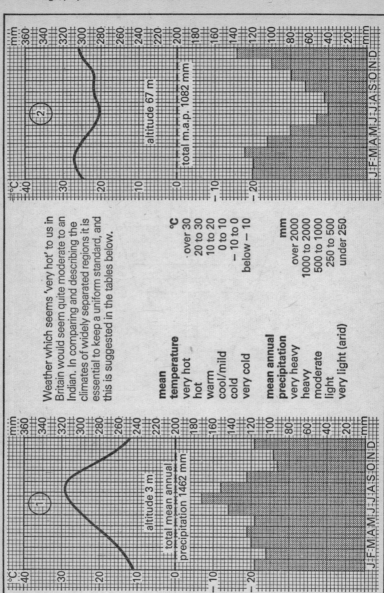

Weather which seems 'very hot' to us in Britain would seem quite moderate to an Indian. In comparing and describing the climates of widely separated regions it is essential to keep a uniform standard, and this is suggested in the tables below.

mean temperature

	°C
very hot	over 30
hot	20 to 30
warm	10 to 20
cool/mild	0 to 10
cold	− 10 to 0
very cold	below − 10

mean annual precipitation

	mm
very heavy	over 2000
heavy	1000 to 2000
moderate	500 to 1000
light	250 to 500
very light (arid)	under 250.

(b) *Explain the differences in climate between any two of the towns. Credit will be given for information added to the map in answering this question.*   (LOND)

You should know from the map what type of climate to expect for each town. Analysing the figures will very quickly yield enough clues to identify each of A,B,C,D. State your findings in an orderly manner for part (*a*). For (*b*) you must *state* the differences before you can *explain* them. Explanation involves describing the factors concerned, and these can largely be shown by labelled arrows (etc) on the map. 'Credit will be given . . .' is a broad hint to do exactly this.

Similar questions require an ability to interpret graphs, eg:

38 *The map shows three natural regions, numbered 1,2,3, in which the temperature and rainfall distribution poses problems to man. The three graphs A,B,C represent climate stations, one in each of regions 1,2,3.*

   (*a*) *In the spaces provided, link each of regions 1,2,3 with the appropriate graph (A,B or C).*
   (*b*) *For each region, describe:*
      (*i*) *the features of the temperature and rainfall distribution which make it different from the others;*
      (*ii*) *the time of year when man is faced with problems caused by the climate.*   (SCOT)

Recognizing climatic types

The following pages contain one or more examples of each type of climate. They are numbered rather than named, so that they can be used in self-testing revision practice. The numbers relate to pages 84–9, where each example is named, located, described and explained. Use the following drill to identify each one:

1 Is the station far above sea level? If so, adjust the temperature as explained on p59.
2 Is the annual range of temperature extremely small? If so, the station is near the Equator.
3 What is the (adjusted) mean annual temperature — and thence how far (roughly) is the station from the Equator?
4 What is the annual range? — and thence how far (roughly) is the station from the sea (p59)?
5 What is the total mean annual precipitation?
6 What is the rainfall regime?

Some types, eg Mediterranean and tropical monsoon, can be recognized at a glance. All are easy to analyse after a little practice. *Warning:* remember the reversal of seasons in the Southern Hemisphere.

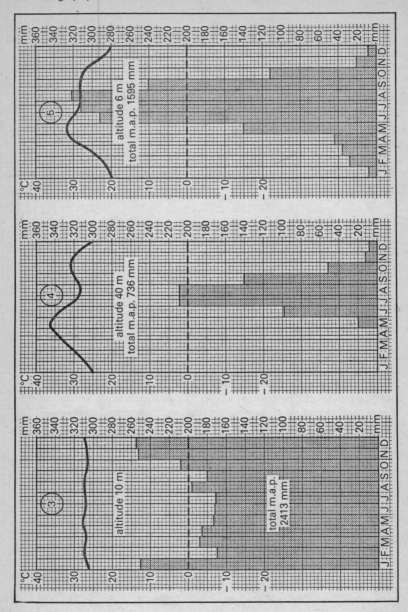

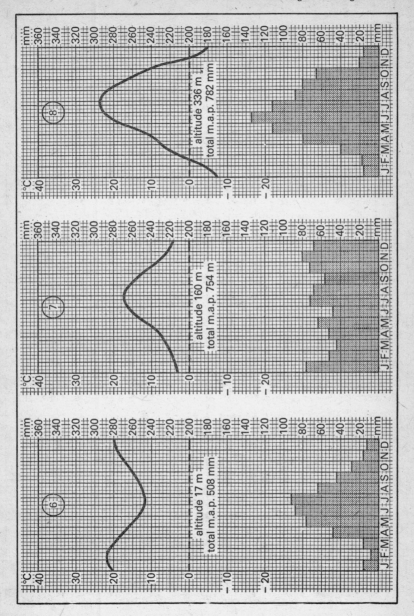

STATION (with altitude)		J	F	M	A	M	J	Jy	A	S	O	N	D	Yr
9 34m	T.°C	27	27	27	27	25	25	24	24	26	26	26	26	—
	P.mm	249	236	335	340	244	13	3	18	104	345	373	249	2509
10 1025m	T.°C	18	19	20	21	22	21	21	21	21	21	20	20	—
	P.mm	23	10	15	33	79	102	109	109	107	109	94	46	836
11 30m	T.°C	29	28	29	29	28	26	25	26	28	29	30	29	—
	P.mm	401	328	256	105	18	3	3	3	12	56	121	261	1567
12 16m	T.°C	−31	−31	−27	−19	−7	2	6	5	−1	−11	−21	−26	—
	P.mm	10	8	10	8	10	13	18	31	23	18	10	8	167
13 128m	T.°C	12	15	18	20	24	28	32	32	30	23	16	13	—
	P.mm	8	14	9	3	—	—	3	12	8	6	8	9	80
14 21m	T.°C	8	11	13	14	17	21	23	22	21	19	12	8	—
	P.mm	97	72	72	36	21	3	—	—	6	21	49	100	477
15 99m	T.°C	11	12	13	16	22	23	26	26	24	20	16	13	—
	P.mm	127	91	66	43	20	5	3	41	31	94	99	89	709

STATION (with altitude)		J	F	M	A	M	J	Jy	A	S	O	N	D	Yr
16 36m	T.°C	4	7	11	17	22	27	30	29	24	19	13	7	—
	P.mm	45	48	95	150	166	244	181	97	71	82	48	28	1255
17 24m	T.°C	2	3	6	8	12	15	17	17	13	9	9	6	—
	P.mm	224	155	135	84	77	69	34	44	105	150	254	199	1530
18 180m	T.°C	−6	−5	0	7	15	18	17	19	14	8	2	−3	—
	P.mm	33	25	40	43	48	66	80	61	45	45	38	38	562
19 665m	T.°C	−14	−11	−5	4	11	14	17	15	10	5	−4	−11	—
	P.mm	23	10	18	23	48	80	85	59	33	18	15	20	432
20 56m	T.°C	−11	−9	−3	5	13	18	21	19	15	8	1	−7	—
	P.mm	94	77	89	64	79	87	94	87	94	85	87	89	1026
21 214m	T.°C	−25	−20	−15	−3	6	13	16	15	8	1	−11	−19	—
	P.mm	15	13	18	15	20	33	56	38	33	23	25	20	309
22 2603m	T.°C	14	14	14	14	14	14	13	14	14	14	14	14	—
	P.mm	59	66	102	147	117	59	51	56	61	158	120	66	1062

The principal climatic types – governing factors, distinctive features and typical vegetation

The names and numbers after each of the following headings are a key to the examples on pp79–83. In each case you must satisfy yourself that the description matches the example(s). A world vegetation map in your textbook or atlas should be carefully compared with the map of climate regions on p75. A useful revision exercise could be the construction of a vegetation diagram corresponding to that on p77.

Use the tables on p79 in making your own expanded notes, with definite numerical values added to the general statements (eg 'heavy rainfall') about each type of climate.

Use your atlas in conjunction with the map on p75 to identify with suitable geographical names (eg 'Indonesia', 'the Amazon Basin', etc) the regions included under each heading.

It must be remembered that such maps and diagrams are very greatly simplified. Within every climate or vegetation region there are large areas where special factors of relief, soil and so on produce exceptions to the rule.

Equatorial Lowland (*Singapore* **3**; *Libreville* (*Gabon*) **9**)   The type extends approx. 5–7° either side of the Equator.

Temperature   Midday sun always high, therefore hot all the year (often slightly moderated by heavy cloud cover). Annual range of temperature (r.o.t.) very small, usually under 3°C. Diurnal r.o.t. about 10°C. A very **equable** climate.

Precipitation   Heavy to very heavy rainfall, well-distributed over the year (though for local reasons some places have a short relatively dry season), and falling usually in heavy convectional showers. Relative humidity very high.

Vegetation **Rain forest** (**selva**).   Tall, high-crowned trees of many different species (p96) form a dense canopy at about 30m above ground level. Shorter trees grow below and between, with an undergrowth of ferns and shrubs and with climbing plants hanging at all levels. Forest is **deciduous**, but with no special season of leaf-fall. Growth is continuous.

Equatorial Highland (*Bogota* (*Colombia*) **22**)

Temperature   Varies with altitude, but annual r.o.t. still very small. Diurnal r.o.t. increases rapidly with altitude and may exceed 30°C.

Precipitation   Varies with aspect and altitude.

Vegetation   Varies with altitude (see above).

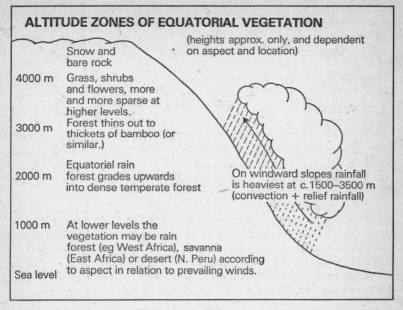

ALTITUDE ZONES OF EQUATORIAL VEGETATION

(heights approx. only, and dependent on aspect and location)

Snow and bare rock

4000 m — Grass, shrubs and flowers, more and more sparse at higher levels.

3000 m — Forest thins out to thickets of bamboo (or similar.)

2000 m — Equatorial rain forest grades upwards into dense temperate forest

On windward slopes rainfall is heaviest at c.1500–3500 m (convection + relief rainfall)

1000 m — At lower levels the vegetation may be rain forest (eg West Africa), savanna (East Africa) or desert (N. Peru) according to aspect in relation to prevailing winds.

Sea level

Tropical Maritime ('Trade Wind Coast') (*Rio de Janeiro* **12**; *Caracas* (*Venezuela*) **10**)   From approx. 6° to 23°N and S on east coasts wherever Trade Winds blow onshore all the year (pp67 and 73).

Temperature   Summers hot to very hot; winters hot. Annual r.o.t. 5–15°C.

Precipitation   Heavy rainfall, mainly convectional, with summer maximum when winds are blowing more strongly into the heated (and therefore low pressure) interior. Total increased by evaporation from warm longshore current (p73).

Vegetation   Rain forest.

Tropical Continental ('Sudan') (*Kayes* (*Mali*) **4**)   From approx. 6° to 23°N and S in continental interiors. Governed by the swing of the wind belts (p67) which bring 'equatorial' summers and 'hot desert' winters.

Temperature   Summer – hot or very hot, winter – warm or hot.

Precipitation   Summer – moderate to heavy convectional rainfall, decreasing with distance from the Equator. Winter – dry.

Vegetation   **Savanna**–coarse tropical grass with varying amounts of tree cover. All vegetation is adapted to the hot wet summers and dry winters: grasses grow, shed their seeds and die; big trees store water (eg baobab); smaller trees have very small leaves to reduce **transpiration** (eg thorn trees).

Tropical Monsoon (*Calcutta* **5;** *Darwin* (*N. Australia*) **11**) In southeast Asia and northern Australia, where land masses lie north and south of an equatorial sea area (p69). Chief factor – the huge size of the Asiatic land mass.

Intense winter cold in the interior ⟶ very high pressure ⟶ outblowing winds reinforcing the N.E. Trade Winds of these latitudes; the offshore winds bring dry winter conditions to coastal regions in southeast Asia and (blowing onshore) heavy summer rainfall to northern Australia, where the normal S.E. Trades are reversed.

Intense summer heat, especially over India, ⟶ very low pressure ⟶ inblowing winds from the mid-latitude high-pressure over Australia and Southern Africa, reversing the normal (N.E. Trades) airflow and bringing exceptionally heavy rain from June to September. Rainfall mainly convectional, increased by relief rain wherever winds cross mountains. Amounts vary with aspect and distance from the sea. However, northern Australia is dry, because prevailing wind is offshore.

Temperature and precipitation There are three seasons: (a) the Cool Season – warm and dry with outblowing winds; (b) the Hot Season – hot to very hot, dry and calm; (c) the Wet Season – hot and wet to very wet, with onshore winds. (*Compare the two examples and note how they complement each other.*)

Vegetation Much as for Tropical Maritime and Tropical Continental, depending on aspect, altitude and distance from the sea; and merging similarly into scrub and desert in the interior.

Hot Desert (*Yuma* (*Arizona*) **13**) From approx. 15° to 30°N and S in western regions of land masses, in latitudes where Trade Winds blow offshore or where (in winter) the mid-latitude high-pressure belt overlies the area.

Temperature Summer – warm nights and very hot days. Winter – cool or cold nights and hot days. Diurnal r.o.t. thus very marked, and night frosts fairly common.

Precipitation Very light, since relative humidity is so low; but heavy night dews are a frequent result of the rapid fall in air temperature after sunset.

Vegetation **Xerophytic** – adapted to hot, dry conditions in various ways such as: small or thorny leaves/deep roots/fleshy, water-storing stems (eg cactus).

Temperate Desert   (*no example given*) Well outside the Tropics are found some arid regions with a wide annual r.o.t., cool or cold winters and warm or hot summers. These temperate deserts occur in a variety of locations, eg the Gobi Desert of Mongolia, which is very remote from the sea; Patagonia, in an intense 'rain shadow' area; some intermontane basins in the northeast United States, also affected by 'rain shadow'.

Warm Temperate Western Margin ('Mediterranean') (*Cape Town* **6**; *Sacramento* (*California*) **14**; *Palermo* (*Sicily*) **15**)   From approx. 30° to 40°N and S on western margins of land masses. Governing factor is the swing of the planetary pressure and wind belts, giving onshore westerlies in winter and high pressure calms in summer.

Temperature   Summers hot, winters mild or warm.
Precipitation   Marked summer drought. Mean annual total light to moderate, mainly frontal in type, often with spring or autumn maximum.
Vegetation   Temperate forest (beech, pine, chestnut) is found in moister, cooler locations such as mountain sides, but more typical plants are those adapted to avoid the summer drought (eg spring-flowering bulbs) or to resist it (eg thick-barked cork oak, thick-barked, deep-rooted olive trees, waxy-leaved laurel).

Warm Temperate Eastern Margin   ('Gulf') (*New Orleans* **1**, *or* **China** – *Wu-han* **16**)   From approx. 23° to 35°–40°N and S on eastern margins of land masses.

Temperature   Summers hot, winters cold to warm.
Precipitation   Moderate to heavy rainfall, usually with marked summer maximum (mainly convectional) from onshore Trade Winds. The 'China' type (Central and Northern China) is much more extreme than the 'Gulf' (of Mexico) type because of the monsoonal reversal of prevailing winds.
Vegetation   Warm temperate evergreen forest – cedar, pine, rhododendron, etc.

Cool Temperate Western Margin ('**Cool Temperate Oceanic**') (*Birmingham* **7**; *Vancouver* (*British Columbia*) **17**)   From approx. 40° to 55°–60°N and S on western margins of land masses. Governing factor is the onshore westerly air stream with frequent **depressions** (*Book 2* pp18–21).

Temperature   Summers – mild or warm; winters – cool or mild. An equable climate, moderated at all seasons by the prevailing winds.

Precipitation   Moderate to heavy rainfall, well-distributed over the year and mainly frontal.

Vegetation   Mixed temperate forest – mainly deciduous, with conifers dominant on higher ground and on poorer soils.

Cool Temperate Eastern Margin ('Laurentian') (*Montreal* 20)

From approx. 35°–40° to 50°N (*no true example in S. Hemisphere*) on eastern margins of land masses. Governing factors are the cold continental interior (in winter) and the cold longshore ocean current (pp72–3).

Temperature   Summers – mild or warm; winters – cold.

Precipitation   Moderate, mainly frontal, and well-distributed (though in eastern Asia the monsoonal influence gives a marked summer maximum). Rain in summer, snow in winter.

Vegetation   Much as previous type but with more conifers.

Continental   (*Omaha* (*USA*) 8; *Kiev* (*USSR*) 18; *Edmonton* (*Canada*) 19)

From approx. 35° to 55°N in continental interiors. Governed by size of land mass, so that typical features are less pronounced in N. America than in Asia, and even less so in the southern continents where the type is hardly distinguishable.

Temperature   A very extreme climate. Summers warm or hot; winters long and cool or cold.

Precipitation   Light to moderate with marked summer maximum, largely convectional. Snow in winter.

Vegetation   Temperate grassland, varying (according to rainfall totals) from tall, rich prairie to poorer, stunted steppe. Tree growth deterred by strong winds as much as by low rainfall. Trees found usually only in sheltered valleys.

Cold Temperate   (*Chipewyan* (*Alberta, Canada*) 21)

From approx. 60°N on western margins, and from approx. 50°N on eastern margins, to 65°–70°N. Governed mainly by latitude, but affected also by warm currents on west and cold currents on east. An extreme climate, despite the misleading name.

Temperature   Summers short, mild or warm; winters long and very cold.

Precipitation   Light, with marked maximum in summer (when winds are better able to reach the interior) and mainly convectional.

Vegetation   **Taiga** – coniferous forest with some hardy deciduous species (birch, willow, etc) in southern fringes. Forest thins out, and trees become stunted, towards the northern limits of the region. Coniferous trees have adapted (a) to the short growing season, by taking two years to produce ripe seeds, and (b) to the cold winters, by developing thin waxy 'needles', which resist frost and shed snow, instead of leaves.

Arctic   (*Arctic Bay* (*Baffin Island*) **12**) On the northern fringes of N. America and Europe/Asia.

Temperature   No month with mean temperature above 10°C. Summers short and cool; winters long and very cold, accentuated by Arctic night and strong winds.

Precipitation   Light, mainly in summer from occasional depressions, and largely as snow.

Vegetation   The brief growing season is more encouraging than might be expected, because the long daylight hours increase the total insolation (diagram p19). Nevertheless the ground never thaws to more than about 50cm deep, below which it remains permanently frozen (**permafrost**). Thus the soil is waterlogged and sour. Only plants which can tolerate these soil conditions, and also withstand the keen winter winds, can survive. Mosses, small flowering shrubs and dwarf trees are typical of this **tundra** vegetation.

The world map overleaf and the following questions relating to it will provide a quick test of your understanding of the two previous chapters. All the questions, including those of the 'multiple choice' type, are typical of those set in recent years by some Boards.

   The answers are printed below. Analyse your mistakes. Where did you go wrong? Do you understand why the answer given is the correct one? If not, re-read the appropriate pages earlier in the book.

Answers:

F   25) d; 26) b; 27) e.
E   a) 18; b) 19; c) 23; d) 20.
D   a) 18; b) 16; c) 17; d) 14.
C   a) 12; b) 9.
B   5) e; 6) b; 7) d; 8) f.
A   1 Labrador (*cold*); 2 Brazil (*warm*); 3 Benguela (*cold*); 4 Kuro Siwo (*warm*).

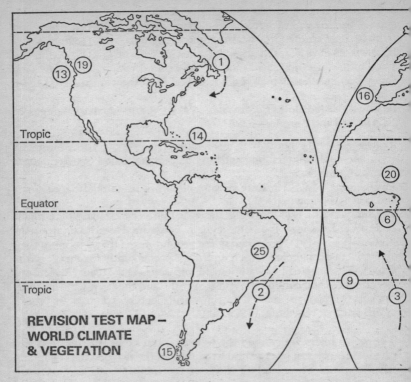

A *Name the ocean currents* **1 2 3 4** *and state whether they are warm or cool.*

B *Four towns are marked and numbered* **5 6 7 8**. *The mean January temperature for each one is included in the list below. Which is which?*
(a) —15°C (b) 27°C (c) —5°C (d) 4°C (e) 11°C (f) 20°C.

C *Four areas are numbered* **9 10 11 12**. *Two of them match the descriptions of atmospheric pressure conditions given below. State the appropriate number for each description.*
(a) *Low pressure in December, high in July.*
(b) *High pressure all the year.*

D *Six areas are numbered* **13 14 15 16 17 18**. *Four of them match the descriptions of prevailing winds given below. State the appropriate number for each description.*
(a) *NW winds in December, SE in July.*
(b) *SW winds in December, calms in July.*
(c) *SE winds all the year.*   (d) *NE winds all the year.*

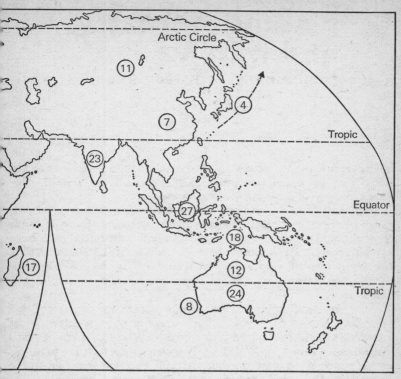

E *Six areas are numbered* **19 20 21 22 23 24.** *Four of them match the descriptions of rainfall regimes given below. State the appropriate number for each description.*

(a) *Summer drought, moderate autumn to spring rainfall.*
(b) *Moderate rainfall at all seasons.*
(c) *Heavy summer rainfall, dry winter.*
(d) *Light summer rainfall, dry winter.*

F *Three areas are numbered* **25 26 27.** *Each can be matched with one of the following descriptions of vegetation. State the appropriate description for each number.*

(a) *Coniferous forest;*   (b) *Desert;*
(c) *Drought-resistant shrubs and mainly evergreen trees.*
(d) *Coarse grassland with scattered trees.*
(e) *Dense forest of tall trees and climbing plants.*
(f) *Temperate grassland.*

6 Fishing, forestry and mining
(including energy resources)

These three activities are among the oldest and most primitive occupations. They are **extractive industries**, concerned with removing for human use part of the Earth's **natural resources**.

Until fairly recently there has been no concern for the future, because further undeveloped resources were always available. Rising demands from a rapidly-growing world population have now forced all nations to realize that the Earth's resources are limited, and that some are already becoming scarce. Recent years have accordingly been marked by concern for **conservation** of those resources; ie for their careful and responsible use.

You must assess, from past examination papers, the degree of detail you may be expected to provide. This varies from a world-wide general knowledge to the specialized case studies expected by some regional syllabuses (eg *Book 2*, pp96, 154–7). This chapter does not aim to supply details which are available in your textbook, so much as to suggest the lines along which your knowledge of those details may be tested.

Fishing

Questions are usually straightforward, eg:

39 *Illustrating your answer with located examples, explain why certain areas specialize in fishing or forestry.*   (LOND)

40 (a) *Japan, Peru and Iceland are among the world's leading fishing nations. Write an account of the fishing industry of one of these countries, referring to such topics as: reasons for importance, types of fish caught, processing.*

    (b) *Explain briefly why some nations wish to extend their fishing limits.*   (SCOT)

41 *The world map provided locates the main commercial fishing grounds.* [The following coastal seas were shaded on the map: E. and W. of N. America; N.W. Africa to N. Norway, inc. Iceland and the

British Isles; N.W. Pacific from Vietnam to Kamchatka; N. Peru.]
(a) *Describe this distribution.*
(b) *Choose* one *country (excluding the British Isles) where sea fishing is important, and show what factors have aided the growth of this activity. Refer to its effect on settlement.*
(c) *The sea supplies only a small part of the world's total food supply. In what ways can it be used more effectively to help overcome the increasing world food shortage, and what factors might endanger such a development?*   (JMB)

Taking the three questions as a whole, three lines of enquiry emerge: 1 Where is commercial fishing important? 2 Why there? 3 What is its future?

To deal with point 1, draw a world sketch-map based on the table below. Shade and name the countries involved and add 'bars' on a scale of 25sq.mm (5×5mm) to 1 per cent of world catch. Learn the map. If your syllabus includes a regional section, make a special study of any important fishing grounds included in it.

Remember that the topic is *commercial* fishing; the table includes only fish landed for sale. Landings by millions of subsistence and spare-time fishermen are not included.

Commercial fisheries – present development
1 **where fish are most plentiful.** Fish feed on other fish, or on **plankton** (tiny forms of animal and vegetable life) which thrives best
   (a) in shallow waters (eg a **continental shelf**);
   (b) in cold polar seas;
   (c) where cold and warm currents mingle;
   (d) on 'cold water coasts' (diagram p73).
2 **where the land is rugged and/or infertile,** thus driving men to seek a living at sea, eg Norway, Newfoundland.

Commercial fishing – leading countries

	% of world total		% of world total
Japan	15	India	3
USSR	13	South Korea, Denmark,	
China	10	Spain	2 each
Peru	5	Indonesia, Thailand, Chile,	
USA	4	Philippines, South Africa,	
5 leading countries	47	UK, Canada,	
		Vietnam	$1\frac{1}{2}$ to 2 each
		Rest of world	about 30
		Total	100

3 **where indented coasts offer many safe harbours** (eg Norway, Japan, British Columbia).

Having once developed because of one or more of these factors, the industry tends to grow in scale if it is located:

4 **in or near seriously overcrowded countries** (eg Japan, China, Indonesia) where food is therefore short; *or*
5 **in or near highly industrialized countries** (eg Japan, USA, USSR, NW Europe) where big cities offer a profitable market.

Using your atlas and textbook, expand these notes into an answer to Q39 or 40(a). Note in particular that all five factors apply to Japan.

Commercial fisheries – the future

Use your textbook and the current news to build up notes on the following problems:

1 **overfishing** Modern methods are so efficient, and demand is so great, that some traditional fisheries are in danger of being 'fished out'; hence (eg) restrictions by Iceland on cod fishing by foreign vessels, and by Britain (in 1977) on herring fishing in the North Sea; and moves by most maritime countries to extend 'fishing limits';
2 **pollution   Industrial effluent** in some sea areas (eg Japan, the Baltic, the Mediterranean) has made fish poisonous;
3 **wasteful use**   Much of the world's catch is processed into livestock feed rather than directly into food for human beings. The outstanding example is Peru, whose undernourished people cannot afford to buy fish and have to export almost all of it to factories in well-fed USA;

and on the following new developments:

4 **fish farming** in coastal and inland waters. (*Not* a new development in southeast Asia, where a rice field often produces as heavy a 'crop' of fish as of rice.) Trout 'farms' have become common in Western countries, and larger-scale schemes may soon be set up, using the warm water from cooling plants of power stations, to stimulate the growth of plaice and other fish of high food quality;
5 **new fishing grounds** being test-fished in many areas;
6 **new types of fish** eg the shrimp-like **krill** of Antarctic waters, which *might* treble the present total world catch.

Forestry

There are three regional types of forest, rather loosely classified as **temperate coniferous** (softwoods), **temperate broad-leaved** (hardwoods) and **tropical broad-leaved** (also hardwoods).

Identify the three types and their regions from your atlas or textbook, and shade them in three different colours on a world sketch-map. Add the names of the countries listed below, with 'bars' constructed as suggested on p93. That for Brazil should be split into $9\frac{1}{2}$ per cent in the (temperate) south and only $1\frac{1}{2}$ per cent in the Amazon selvas. *Learn the map*.

Make sure, from pp84–9 and from your textbook, that you can describe the main species and characteristics of each type of forest and explain their relation to the climate. We are not concerned with rubber, cocoa and other such tree products, but only with trees felled for their wood.

The lumbering industry

About 70 per cent of all hardwood is still cut for fuel. The rest is used in (eg) fine quality furniture and building work, boats and hundreds of other specialized products such as cricket bats. Softwood is cut for building, for cheap furniture, matches, boxes, etc, and increasingly as 'pulp-wood' for the paper and rayon industries.

Timber production – leading countries

Softwood – world total 1100 million m³		Hardwood – world total 1350 million m³	
USSR	29 per cent	Brazil	11 per cent
USA	21	Indonesia	10
Canada	11	India	9
China	8	China	7·5
Sweden	4·5	USA	6
Brazil, Finland, Japan	2 each	Nigeria, USSR	5 each
Rest of Europe	10	Other equatorial countries	17
Rest of world	10·5	Europe	14
		Rest of world	15·5
	100%		100%

If your syllabus includes a regional section, prepare for detailed questions on the region's forests and forest industries. Many questions on this topic, however, are general, such as 38 on p92. Another type of question frequently asked is:

42 (a) *On the world map provided, name and locate the position and*
extent of (i) an area of equatorial rain forest; (ii) an area of taiga
(N. Hemisphere coniferous forest).

(b) *For each, describe the main characteristics of the vegetation.*

(c) *State the problems which arise in the exploitation of timber resources*
in each type of forest. (JMB)

Part (a) is simple if you have learnt the map as suggested (accuracy is
important). Part (b) is equally straightforward. In preparation for topics
like (c), find details with which to amplify the following summary:

Problems of lumbering in the selvas

1 Hot, unhealthy climate (*give details*) discouraging active physical work.
2 Remoteness, in most areas, from a suitable source of labour and from
industrial markets.
3 Lack of adequate transport except near rivers (and some species too
heavy to float).
4 Variety of species – trees of one kind often widely separated, so
felling and removal, through dense undergrowth and over wet ground,
difficult and costly. Only valuable timber is worth removal, and
taking one tree may involve damaging or destroying acres of virgin
forest. Large-scale operations thus often lead to serious soil erosion.
5 Slow growth of useful species discourages long-term plans for
reafforestation.

Problems of lumbering in the taiga

1 Harsh winters (*give figures*) in remote camps are not popular.
2 Remoteness and – 3 Transport – much as in the selvas *except* near
developed, industrialized areas – which have long ago been cleared
of trees.
4 In the more northerly taiga, slow, scattered and stunted tree growth
due to climate.

Advantages of the taiga

1 growth of coniferous trees in great numbers of one species together;
2 quick growth in the southerly fringes;
3 many rivers suitable for generating hydro-electricity as well as for
floating logs, eg in Sweden and Canada.

Conservation, plant research and reafforestation have resulted in most
softwood now coming from forests which have already been cleared at
least once. In some countries regrowth is now keeping pace with felling.

Mining and minerals

This heading covers a wide range of vitally important resources and activities. Before considering particular examination topics we must summarize a few general considerations.

Types of mineral

Minerals are substances forming part of the Earth's crust; and more particularly, substances useful enough to be worth mining. They fall into five classes:

1 **building materials** such as stone, clay (for bricks and tiles) and sand, gravel and limestone (for cement and concrete); and other similar materials such as pottery clay and road stone. Occasional questions are set on this topic in relation to the British Isles.
2 **metals**, of which iron is by far the most important, being the basic material of modern industrial society. Aluminium, copper, zinc and lead, in that order, come next in quantity of production, but iron is mined and smelted in amounts many times greater than that of all other metals combined.
3 **non-metallic minerals used in the chemical industries** such as limestone, sulphur, potash and salt.
4 **fuels** – coal, lignite, natural gas and petroleum; also the radioactive metals used as nuclear fuels.
5 **water**   This may seem an odd place in which to refer to what is (except for air) the most essential of all natural resources, but water is a mineral and is very often obtained by mining.

Mineral deposits

May occur in:

1 **veins or lodes** – fissures and cracks into which minerals, usually metals, have been injected as gases or liquids by igneous action (p25) and have later solidified.
2 **beds** or **seams** – strata formed by one mineral (eg coal) or strata permeated by a concentration of a mineral resulting from leaching (p36) or other similar process; eg many iron ores.
3 **alluvial** or **placer** deposits – concentrations of a particular mineral which has been eroded from a vein or seam and the resulting debris redeposited in the alluvium of a stream or lake bed. Malayan tin and Siberian gold are mostly found in this form.

Mining methods

The main methods of mineral extraction are:

1 **opencast** or **strip-mining**, used where deposits are near the surface and so can be reached by removal of shallow surface layers of **overburden**. Used mainly for coal and iron mining. The term **quarrying** is used for opencast mining of chalk, sand, stone, etc.

2 **adit** or **drift mining**, used where deposits are most easily reached by horizontal or sloping tunnels into a hillside.

3 **shaft mining**, used to reach deposits at depth. Vertical shafts are sunk and horizontal galleries extended underground to extract the minerals. The most expensive form of mining.

4 **drilling** a deep hole is the normal way to extract oil, gas and underground water.

Factors involved in mining

Many mineral deposits which were discovered long ago have not yet been mined. Many existing mines have been closed before their mineral deposits were exhausted. In each case one or more of the following factors is responsible:

1 *availability* Is there enough to justify the high cost of opening a mine? Is the mineral in a usable form? (for example, the huge iron ore-fields of Lorraine and Luxembourg were useless for steel-making until 1878, when the discovery of a cheap process for removing their phosphorus content made the ore worth mining.

2 *accessibility* Does suitable transport exist, or can it be provided, to move the mined product to market cheaply enough? The answer often depends as much on the value per tonne of the product as on the cost of transport. Gold can stand higher transport costs than clay.

A valuable deposit may be worth spending huge sums to make accessible; eg the railway from Sept Iles to the Quebec/Labrador iron ore fields. Conversely, though, a change in the cost of transport can revolutionize a mining industry; eg the use of 'bulk carriers' to ship coal from Australia to Europe and Japan at very low cost per tonne.

Both 1 and 2 depend largely on:

3 *demand* How much are customers prepared to pay? Many mines open, close and reopen at intervals, depending on the world price of their product. The Cornish tin mines have offered an excellent illustration of this factor in the 1970s. (See also *Book 2* p153.)

Metals

The principal metals fall into four groups:

1 **precious**, ie gold, silver, platinum.
2 **radio-active**, ie potential nuclear fuels such as uranium.
3 **ferrous**, ie iron, and the steel refined from it.
   Iron's primary quality is its *strength*. It is also:
(a) relatively cheap, as it forms a major part of the Earth's crust.
   Workable deposits of iron ore (rock containing a useful proportion
   of iron) large enough and accessible enough to bear the heavy cost
   of mining and transport, are widespread.
(b) versatile. Treated in various ways, often by mixing with **alloys** –
   other metals such as vanadium and tungsten – it can be made
   springy, sharp, rustproof, tough, etc, as required.
4 **non-ferrous**, or literally 'not iron'; but in general, the other
   industrial metals used on a large scale, ie aluminium, copper, zinc,
   lead and tin.

Aluminium, like iron, is a very common element. Its main ore is
bauxite. Until recently, however, aluminium was scarce and expensive
(*see diagram p103*) because the refining process requires large quantities
of electricity which were not generally available. The very rapid increase
in output reflects the useful qualities of aluminium – strength, lightness,
resistance to corrosion and electrical conductivity. Bauxite contains very
little aluminium per tonne. Thus, to save transport costs, it is usually
concentrated (partially refined) into **alumina** before it leaves the mine.

Copper was probably the first metal to be worked by early Man. It is
easily refined and worked, does not rust and has high electrical conductivity. The electrical industry consumes over half the world output,
but aluminium is now cheaper and to some extent is replacing it. As with
bauxite, copper ore usually contains very little metal – often less than
2 per cent – and partial refining at the mine is normal.

Zinc has many uses, mainly as 'galvanized' rustproof coating for steel
products such as buckets, pipes, wire netting and corrugated sheets.

Lead ore is always found with zinc ore, but rarely in the same proportion. Its main advantages are resistance to corrosion, ease in working
and non-conductivity. There is a growing world shortage, largely
because of the increased use in motor vehicle batteries. In some traditional uses, such as roofing and plumbing, lead has largely been replaced
by cheaper materials.

Tin has always been scarce and expensive, and is used almost entirely
as an anti-corrosion coating for steel. Total world production is quite
small (c. 250,000 tonnes p.a.) and is likely to fall in the near future.

All six of these metals, together with gold and silver, may be mentioned in short-answer, general knowledge type questions. You should therefore know the main producing countries, the main centres within those countries and the conditions and methods of production.

Wider questions on metal mining and manufacture often relate to particular regions or topics; eg the importance of gold in the development of South Africa. General world questions are limited largely to iron/steel, bauxite/aluminium and (less often) copper. The following examples illustrate the range of knowledge tested:

43 *The tables* [similar to those on p102] *show the amount of bauxite and aluminium produced in a recent year.*
   (a) *Locate by a sketch-map one area listed in the table where bauxite is mined, and describe and account for the method of mining iu the chosen location.*
   (b) *Explain why some leading producers of bauxite do not produce large amounts of aluminium.*
   (c) *Select* one *important centre for aluminium production in the countries listed (outside the UK) and with the help of a sketch-map state the conditions that have assisted the growth of the industry there.* (JMB)

44 (a) *On the world map provided, mark and name* one *area of large-scale iron ore production and* one *area of large-scale copper production* (both outside the UK).
   (b) *For each mineral give an account of the geographical factors which have affected its exploitation in the area you have chosen, describing any difficulties encountered and stating how they are being overcome.*
   (c) *Suggest why it is found necessary to develop mineral resources in difficult areas.* (JMB)

45 *Study the statistics* [similar to those given opposite] *for the production of iron ore and steel.*
   (a) *Describe the main features of the distribution of (i) iron ore production, and (ii) steel production.*
   (b) *Name, from the lists,* one *major iron ore producer which is not a major steel producer, and suggest why it is (i) a major iron ore producer; (ii) not a major steel producer.*
   (c) *Choose* one *steel-producing area from within one of the steel-producing countries listed (other than the UK) and, with the aid of a sketch-map, describe and account for the location and growth in that area of industries* dependent upon steel. (JMB)

WORLD
IRON ORE PRODUCTION
(*world total (actual metal content) c 510m tonnes*)

USSR	27½%
Australia	12½
Brazil	9
USA	9
	58
China	7
Liberia	5
Canada	5
India	4½
Sweden	4
Venezuela	3½
France	3
South Africa	1½
Rest of world	8½
	100

WORLD
STEEL PRODUCTION
(*world total c 725m tonnes*)

USSR	21%
USA	18
Japan	16½
West Germany	7
	62½
China	4½
France	4½
UK	3½
Italy	3
Poland	2
Czechoslovakia	2
Belgium	2
Canada	2
Rest of world	14
	100

Compare the lists of iron ore and steel producers. Construct a world sketch-map on the lines suggested on p93 (using two distinct colours or symbols) to illustrate the distribution of the iron ore mining and steel refining industries.

Notice the much greater production of steel than of the ore from which it is refined. This apparent absurdity is explained by the large amount of scrap metal salvaged and recycled in most steel-making countries. In Britain this amounts to half the total steel output.

The twelve countries named in the lists produce 91¼ per cent of the world's iron ore and 85¼ per cent of its steel. How many countries are leading producers of both ore and steel?

How much of (a) the ore and (b) the steel comes from the three southern continents? Do your answers confirm what you already know of the relative degree of industrial development of the northern and southern continents?

Four parts of the world are heavily industrialized: North America, Europe, USSR and Japan; with China rapidly nearing a similar scale of output. Which of the listed steel producers does not belong to one of these five groups?

Before preparing answers to the questions on the opposite page, consider the following points.

Q43(a) and 44(a) and (b) call for general world knowledge *and* for details of at least one centre of production in each case. Such details should be found in your textbook, augmented if possible by a knowledge of current affairs. 'Geographical factors' include not only physical factors (relief, remoteness or otherwise, climate, etc), which either help or hinder development, but also the presence or absence of good transport links, firm government and other human factors. The latter have been well illustrated in recent years by the problems of the Zambia-Zaire 'Copperbelt'.

Q43(b), 44(c) and 45(a)(b) all make the same point; many countries with rich mineral resources have not (yet) developed the industrial capacity to use them; while some leading industrial nations lack the minerals they need, and so have gone far afield to exploit new resources in other countries. As always, answers of this kind must be illustrated by named examples, of which Japan is perhaps the most striking example.

Q43(c) and 45(c) demand a detailed knowledge of regional examples, but a study of these statistics and diagrams will be useful. They will also help in answering Q45(a).

BAUXITE (world – 80m tonnes)		ALUMINIUM (world – 16m tonnes)		HYDRO- ELECTRIC POWER	
Australia	26%	USA	31%	USA	23%
Guinea	15	USSR	13	Canada	14
Jamaica	14	Japan	9	USSR	12
USSR	8	W. Germany	6	Japan	6
Surinam	6	Canada	4	Norway	5
Hungary	4	Norway	4	Brazil	4·5
Guyana	4	UK	3	France	4
Greece	3	France	3	Sweden	3
France	3	Italy	2	Italy	3
Yugoslavia	2	Netherlands	2	Spain	2
Others	15	Others	23	Others	23·5
	100%		100%		100%

Construct a world sketch-map to illustrate the bauxite mining and aluminium refining industries. How many of the countries listed are leading producers (a) of both bauxite and aluminium? (b) of both aluminium and hydro-electricity? (c) of all three? Do your answers seem to support the statements made on p99?

PRINCIPAL NON-FERROUS METALS
World production 1875–1975

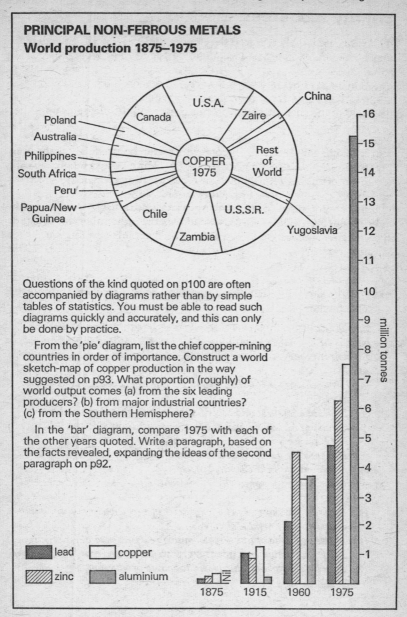

Questions of the kind quoted on p100 are often accompanied by diagrams rather than by simple tables of statistics. You must be able to read such diagrams quickly and accurately, and this can only be done by practice.

From the 'pie' diagram, list the chief copper-mining countries in order of importance. Construct a world sketch-map of copper production in the way suggested on p93. What proportion (roughly) of world output comes (a) from the six leading producers? (b) from major industrial countries? (c) from the Southern Hemisphere?

In the 'bar' diagram, compare 1975 with each of the other years quoted. Write a paragraph, based on the facts revealed, expanding the ideas of the second paragraph on p92.

Energy resources

This term has largely replaced the phrase 'fuel and power', though both may be met in textbooks and examination papers. The topic has become so crucial since the early 1970s that you are almost certain to face a question on it, either in a general world context or in relation to regional studies. You must therefore have a clear understanding of the terms used and of the changes and problems implied in the diagrams opposite.

Primary energy sources

Fuel, in burning, releases energy which can be used (a) for heating (eg in houses, or for cooking) or (b) for providing **power** (eg for driving steam- or oil-powered machines, or for generating electricity). Both (a) and (b) are essential uses of **primary energy**.

Until recent times wind, moving water and muscle were the only energy sources available, just as wood was the only important fuel. All these energy sources are **renewable**. The diagrams opposite show that we now rely overwhelmingly on **non-renewable** mineral fuels. The 'energy crisis', so often mentioned in the news, arises from the unsolved problem of how we shall fare when the world's stock of those fuels is exhausted. Naturally, therefore, questions on this topic often hinge on current changes.

46 *In what ways is the economic geography of Great Britain likely to be influenced by (i) the exploitation of the large deposits of oil and natural gas beneath the North Sea; (ii) the relative decrease in the demand for coal?*   (O & C)

47 (a) *Give reasons for the changing importance of coal and oil as sources of energy.*
    (b) *Explain how these and other factors have affected production in one* named coalfield *and one* named oilfield *(outside the UK in each case).*
    (c) *How has the use of oil as a raw material affected the location and development of the chemical industry?*   (JMB)

48 *Study the bar graphs of world energy consumption in recent years.* [See overleaf.]
    (a) *Describe the changes in the character of world energy consumption. Give reasons for these changes.*
    (b) *Name one* area of large-scale mining *and one* area of large-scale HEP production *(outside the UK in each case) and for each area describe the factors which have favoured production.*   (JMB)

CHANGES IN WORLD ENERGY CONSUMPTION

In 1877 the 'Age of Steam' was already at its height. Europe and the eastern USA were already industrialized, and railways and steamships were common in many parts of the world. The dramatic changes in the following century, illustrated by the diagrams, resulted from population increase, the spread of mechanisation and higher standards.

1 World population trebled during the century, and doubled between 1940 and 1977 alone.
2 Manufacturing and transport are now mechanized throughout much of the world. The energy of human and animal muscles and of the wind has been superseded by fuel-powered machines.
3 On average, each member of the greatly-increased world population now has a much higher material standard of living, made possible only by a much higher output of manufactured goods, which in turn depends on a much higher rate of consumption of energy by industry and transport.

These diagrams are drawn in terms of **coal equivalent**, ie the amount of coal needed to produce a proportionate share of total energy output.

wood and peat
nuclear
H.E.P.
natural gas
oil
lignite
coal

1975

1940

1875

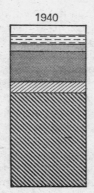

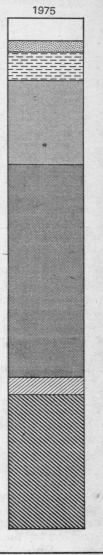

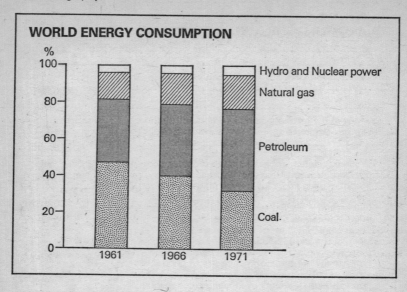

WORLD ENERGY CONSUMPTION

Q46 is typical of many set in regional papers. 47 and 48 are typical of 'general' papers; but it should be noted that detailed knowledge of specific examples is still called for. Here, as with other topics, the ground covered by your own syllabus must be thoroughly prepared.

In interpreting diagrams like those above it is important to distinguish between percentages and actual quantities. The 'bars' are all the same size, since each one represents 100 per cent of the **energy mix** in the year stated. Total consumption increased, however, by 50 per cent in the decade covered by the diagrams. Thus the quantities for 1971 were all much greater in comparison with 1961 than it would appear. Coal consumption obviously declined *relatively* (in the words of Q45) but *absolutely* it increased by 10 per cent.

The question is quite a fair one since it asks about the 'character' of world energy consumption and not about quantities; and the main change, ie the greatly increased consumption of petroleum and natural gas, is clearly shown.

Supplies and future prospects

Questions on coal, oil and hydro-electricity (HEP) are set much more often than on natural gas and **lignite**. The following details will assist revision. All five energy sources should be studied in relation to any regional section of the syllabus.

Coal The tables and accompanying questions underline some essential facts about the world distribution of coal. The predominance of three countries in the 'reserves' table is partly, but not entirely, a reflection of these countries' huge size. Note the high position still held by Britain despite two centuries of intensive mining.

Be careful in answering questions like 46(a). Coal's 'changing importance' from about 1950 to 1973 was its *relative* decline (*but see p106*) during a world glut of cheap oil and gas. The situation is now changing yet again, with a general realization that oil and gas will soon be very scarce and dear. 1975 coal production is expected to be doubled by the year 2000.

Depending on the future rate of increase, the world has enough coal for several centuries to come. Coal can, rather expensively, be converted into oil and gas, and scientists are urgently seeking ways of doing this more cheaply. If they succeed, the reserves will obviously be used up much sooner.

COAL

What percentage of (a) annual production and (b) reserves is in the three southern continents? Construct a world sketch map to illustrate both tables. Which of the five major industrial centres (*p102*) does *not* appear in these lists? What does the 'reserves' list suggest about the possible future of the other four major centres?

Annual production (%)		Estimated reserves (%)	
USSR	28	USSR	60
USA	24	USA	15
China	16	China	14
Poland	7	West Germany	3
UK	5	Poland	2
India	4	UK	2
West Germany	3½	India	1
South Africa	3	South Africa	1
Australia	3	Rest of world	2
Rest of Europe	3		
Rest of world	3½		100
	100		

Factors affecting production in a given coalfield (47(b)) and (48(b)) are almost all connected with the cost of delivery to consumers, since coal is not mined unless it can be sold. They are:

1 **mining conditions** Thick, continuous and level coal seams are cheaper to work than thin, faulted and contorted seams; eg coal from the Appalachian coalfield of eastern USA can be delivered to the steelworks at Dunkirk more cheaply than coal from French mines less than an hour's journey inland. Likewise, opencast or adit mining is cheaper than deep shaft mining; and large coalfields produce cheaper coal, per tonne, than small separate 'pockets'.

2 **location**   Many coalfields were developed, as a result of changing technology, to serve existing industries; eg the Lancashire coalfield enabled steam to replace water power in the cotton mills. Easy access to deep water, eg from the Appalachian or New South Wales coalfields, makes export cheaper.

3 **transport**   Improved facilities, eg bigger 'bulk carrier' ships or 'merry-go-round' trains, may make the difference between profit and loss for a particular mine.

4 **government policy**   Old mines may be kept open by government assistance beyond their profitable life, in order to minimize unemployment and other social problems; eg some South Wales mines since 1947.

Petroleum   The best answer to Q46(b) is perhaps to name and describe one of the many oilfields (eg the Alaska North Slope field) which would not have been developed at all except for the growing pressure of the 'energy crisis'.

Oil exploration teams are working in the Arctic, in the Amazon forests and in the central Sahara; and a third of the world's oil already comes from 'offshore' fields. The search has become so desperately urgent that no physical conditions are severe enough to deter it.

Since immense reserves have already been found, this may seem odd. It is explained by:

1 **the continued growth in demand**   Doubling its consumption every ten years, the world uses more oil in every fresh decade than in the whole of previous history. A serious shortage is forecast for the early twenty-first century.

2 **declining production in the USA**, which for many years was the leading producer, and is still by far the largest consumer.

3 **the location of known reserves**, of which more than half are in the Middle East, a region of political unrest threatened constantly by war. OPEC (*the Organisation of Petroleum Exporting Countries*) is dominated by Middle Eastern states. Europe, Japan and the USA depend largely on Middle East supplies, and the USSR may soon do so. OPEC will be able to dictate terms to the industrialized world unless huge alternative sources of energy are found. (See also *Book 2* pp51, 92, 128–32.)

Annual production
(%)

USSR	19
Saudi Arabia	15
USA/Canada	18
Iran	11
Venezuela	4
Iraq	4
Kuwait	4
Rest of Middle East	5
Africa (excl. Egypt)	10
Europe	4
Rest of world	6
	100

PETROLEUM
Construct a world sketch-map to illustrate these figures.

What proportion of annual production is (a) from the Middle East? (b) from the industrialized regions named on p102?

Under 5 per cent of world oil production is used in the Middle East. What conclusions can be drawn from this fact? See note (3) opposite.

Estimated reserves
(%)

Middle East	60
USA/Canada	8
USSR	8
Africa	8
Latin America	6
Rest of world	10
	100

Secondary energy

This is the term used for electricity, which requires a primary energy source for its generation. All developed countries now depend on electricity as much as on oil. Power stations may be:

1 **thermal** The generators are driven by steam heated by coal, oil, gas, lignite or even (eg in Ireland) peat. The fuel chosen for a new power station depends mainly on cost, delivered to the station; partly on other considerations such as the need to avoid unemployment in the coalfields. An important point is that thermal plants can use fuels which are of little value for other purposes, such as lignite and poor coal.

2 **nuclear** Running costs are low, but the initial building cost, unsolved technical problems and public concern about its dangers have prevented nuclear power from developing as fast as was expected. It is unlikely, in present forms, to bridge the coming 'energy gap'. Nuclear fusion using water as fuel may, however, eventually replace the present nuclear fission process. It would be cheap, safe and free from fuel supply problems; but the necessary technology will take many years to develop.

3 **hydro-electric** Power stations (table on p102) produce only about 4 per cent of world output. This proportion is not likely to increase. Although 'free' and constantly renewed, water power has problems of its own: (a) a reliable and constant 'head' of water must be maintained. This usually requires a dam as well as a power station. The initial cost is thus much higher than that of a thermal plant.

(b) a dam can be built only where the rock foundations are firm enough to stand the tremendous pressure of the structure plus the water impounded behind it. (c) an HEP reservoir 'drowns' land which is probably valued for other purposes, thus further increasing the cost. If the land is unused, this is probably because the location is remote, which in turn raises problems of access, labour supply, etc. Really large HEP schemes usually form part of a much greater development which in any case is located in a remote region; eg the lumber and mining projects of the Canadian Shield. (d) the obvious and easy sites have already been developed. Future schemes will thus be progressively more costly. Many of them, however, will no doubt be carried out when the need becomes more pressing.

4 **alternative sources** Various other ways of generating electricity are in use or under active research. They include **geo-thermal** power, sunlight, winds, waves and tides. You should know something about each, with examples. None of these sources seems likely to make a substantial contribution to world energy supplies before the end of the century.

Make sure you can draw and label a detailed cross-section diagram of a coal mine and an oil well (showing the geological formations involved) and of an HEP dam and plant.

Questions like 47 on p104 may occur, *but related to the 'energy mix' for electrical generation* rather than to primary sources in general. Read all questions very carefully.

Water

Water for drinking is obviously an essential requirement. Occasional regional questions are set on the water supplies of a particular city, and Los Angeles is a good example to use.

Rivers are in most cases the major source of water supply, with underground water (p41) a useful secondary source. Sea-water **desalination** is so far an expensive rarity. In some dry areas such as the Sahara and central Australia, artesian basins may be the major or indeed the only source. Both surface and ground water supplies are becoming depleted in many places as population pressure increases.

Water is required not only for drinking but also for:

1 **industrial use** Enormous quantities are needed, simply for cooling, by (eg) oil refineries, steelworks and power stations. All factories

need a copious supply which for some processes (eg paper making or brewing) must be of a high standard of cleanliness.

2 **waste disposal**   Sewage and industrial effluent have always been dumped in the nearest stream. The need for pre-treatment to avoid pollution of water supplies is now clearly recognized by most advanced countries.

3 **irrigation** is no longer limited to desert regions, but is used in damp climates as dissimilar as Britain and Uganda to 'top up' the natural rainfall and thus increase crop production (p121).

4 **electricity generation** (already discussed).

5 **transport**   Deep-water access by sea or river is a most important factor in the location of many modern industries (eg the steel industry of eastern North America).

6 **fishing** makes a valuable contribution to food supplies in many inland regions (eg the Great Lakes of East and Central Africa).

7 **recreation** on water (angling, sailing, rowing, swimming, etc) is a prominent feature of modern life.

8 **flood control**   Most rivers have seasonal periods when much of their water reaches the sea unused. A dam prevents flood water from endangering life and property downstream, and holds it back to serve useful purposes later.

River management schemes thus involve **multi-purpose development** (*Book 2* pp154–7). The more uses a scheme makes possible, the lower the cost of each one; on this basis many HEP projects are carried out which would be too costly on their own. All these ideas should be kept in mind when answering questions such as:

49 *Write an essay on multi-purpose river development.*   (LOND)

50 *For a multi-purpose river development scheme you have studied: (i) draw a sketch-map to show the location of the scheme; (ii) explain how its completion has helped agriculture and industrial development.*   (AEB)

Choice of examples will depend on your syllabus. It is wise to prepare two in detail, one from the 'developed' countries (eg the Rhône-Saône, Volga, Tennessee or Columbia Rivers), and one from the 'Third World' (eg Nile, Zambesi, Indus or Ganges).

7 Farming

The word **agriculture** may mean 'farming in general', or it may signify the cultivation of crops as distinct from **pastoralism,** which is the rearing of livestock. A study of farming, the most vital of all human occupations, naturally forms part of any geography syllabus. It may appear as an aspect of regional study, or as a general world survey, or both. Some special topics and problems are dealt with in *Book 2*. This short chapter summarizes the basic knowledge against which any detailed revision should be undertaken. It is in some sense a continuation of Chapter 5, and of pp122–3 in particular, and should be read in relation to the regional summary on pp84–9.

Farm products
Your syllabus may require you to be familiar with (eg) 'the animals and plants of major economic importance'; or it may specify a number of farm products for special study on a world basis. Even if there is no specific syllabus requirement, a general knowledge of the topic is desirable. Check, well before the examination, whether to expect questions such as:

51 *Illustrating your answer with located examples, explain why certain areas specialize in—*
   (a) beef production *or* dairying;
   (b) fruit farming *or* viticulture.   (LOND)
52 *Describe and explain, with the aid of a sketch-map, the world distribution of rice growing.*   (SUJB)
53 [Part of a multiple-choice question (see p11)]
   Six areas [on the world map supplied] *are numbered C1, C2, C3, C4, C5, C6. Three of these can be matched with the descriptions given below. Write the appropriate number after each description.*
      An area where large quantities of wheat are grown.
      An area where large quantities of maize are grown.
      An area where large numbers of dairy cattle are kept.   (OX)

Notice the need for factual knowledge of examples, expressed mainly in map form; and for explanation, ie for an understanding of the factors involved (*see summary, p116*). Q53 does not actually require a statement of these factors, but a candidate who is aware of them is likely to do better than one who tries to guess three out of six!

Decide, with reference to your syllabus, how many of the following major commodities you should include in your revision:

Cereals: wheat, rice, maize.

Fruit: apples, citrus fruit, bananas.

Livestock products: beef, lamb, butter, cheese, wool.

Beverages: tea, coffee, cocoa, wine (vine-growing is **viticulture**).

Vegetable oils: soya beans, cotton-seed, linseed, groundnuts (*peanuts*), copra, olives, palm oil.

Sugar: (cane and beet).

Cotton.

Rubber.

In each case you should make notes of the leading producers (best done in map form, on the lines already suggested) and of the circumstances (climatic, seasonal, technical, etc) in which production is maintained. These circumstances vary widely: eg wheat may be a fully-mechanized summer crop (Canada) or a hand-cultivated winter crop (northern India). Note also the special problems of individual producing regions: eg boll weevil in the former 'Cotton Belt' of the USA.

For wheat, rice, bananas, livestock products and coffee, if not for other commodities, some knowledge of the major exporting and importing countries is desirable. As usual, a labelled world sketch-map is the most memorable way of summarizing such facts, using a good economic atlas as well as a textbook.

Farming methods
Before considering farming in detail, three broad classifications must be recognized. These are not separate divisions but different ways of looking at the same broad scene.

1 **Agriculture or pastoralism?**   The distinction is usually rather blurred, since most livestock farmers cultivate at least some crops (eg hay) and most cultivators rear at least a few chickens.

54 The maps, diagrams and information below concern two contrasting farms in the Tweed Basin.
  (a) Describe and explain the difference in the amount of land used for arable farming on the two farms.
  (b) With reference to both farms, explain the phrase: 'Upland farms rear livestock; lowland farms prepare them for market'.   (SCOT)

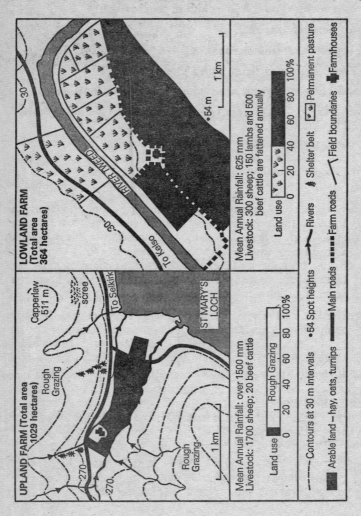

UPLAND FARM (Total area 1029 hectares)

Capperlaw 511 m

scree

Rough Grazing

ST MARY'S LOCH

To Selkirk

Rough Grazing

Mean Annual Rainfall: over 1500 mm
Livestock: 1700 sheep; 20 beef cattle

Land use

Rough Grazing

0 20 40 60 80 100%

----- Contours at 30 m intervals   •54 Spot heights
█ Arable land – hay, oats, turnips   Main roads

LOWLAND FARM (Total area 364 hectares)

RIVER TWEED

To Kelso

•54 m

1 km

Mean Annual Rainfall: 625 mm
Livestock: 300 sheep; 150 lambs and 500 beef cattle are fattened annually

Land use

🐑 🐑 🐑

0 20 40 60 80 100%

🐑 Shelter belt   Permanent pasture
Rivers   ··· Field boundaries   Farmhouses
Shelter belt   Farm roads

2 Subsistence or commercial farming?   A few primitive societies
are still **subsistence** farmers, ie entirely dependent for food and
clothing on their crops and/or livestock; but these are now very rare.
Even in the 'Third World', where most people are poor peasants,
almost all sell at least some of their produce to pay taxes, buy salt, etc.
Farming in the developed countries is almost entirely **commercial**,
geared to the sale of cash crops, livestock and livestock products.

3 Extensive or intensive?   To increase production, a farmer may
extend his activities over more land, using the same resources of
labour, machinery, fertilizer, etc. He will hope to get a greater return
in total, though less from each hectare. Alternatively he may **intensify**
the use of the land he already owns. By putting more resources into
each hectare he hopes to reap a greater reward from the same area.
This is the distinction between extensive and intensive farming of all
kinds. Examples will be found on pp118–21.

The part-question quoted opposite is a good example of this contrast;
and of a type of question which is increasingly being set by some Boards,
requiring the ability to interpret farm maps and statistics.

Study both maps, noting that much of the 'rough grazing' area of the
upland farm is not shown. Study also the data supplied.

Compare the relief of the two farms. Which offers the better scope
for mechanical cultivation?

Compare the rainfall. How is soil on the slopes of the upland farm
likely to be affected in (a) thickness and (b) fertility?

Compare the altitude. How must this affect the climate and the seasonal work of the upland farm?

Answering part (a), state the *proportion*, and from this the actual
amount, of arable land on each farm:

 (i) upland: about 5% of 1029ha=about 50ha.
(ii) lowland: about 60% of 364ha=about 220ha.

What do you think happens to the crops in each case? Which farmer
uses more resources per 100ha in cultivation? Why is this (presumably)
profitable in the one case, yet not attempted in the other? What is the
proportion of (a) sheep (b) lambs (c) cattle per 100ha in each case? Can
you explain the difference?

Scottish hill farmers sell their sheep and cattle mainly to other
(lowland) farmers rather than to slaughterers. Can you now (answering
Q54 (b)) explain why? On which farm would you expect the land,
per hectare, to be the more valuable?

Factors affecting farming

Many questions, especially those relating to regional studies, are similar to:

55 For each of (a) dairy farming and (b) extensive wheat farming, name one area in North America where it is a major activity and give reasons for its development in this area.   (AEB)

A sketch-map to define each area you have chosen is clearly essential. It should include enough names (chief towns, rivers, etc) to identify its extent fairly precisely, and should be labelled to indicate the main factors, climatic or otherwise, which account for its importance.

These factors will be the 'reasons' you are asked to supply. They will be among the following, which influence every farmer's choice as to the use of his land. The physical factors are usually the most obvious, but the human factors must always be considered and are sometimes vital.

See also the summary maps in *Book 2* p41, (British Isles), p87 (Western Europe), and p124 (North America), which cover the topic in a generalized way.

Physical factors

1 **Climate: total mean annual rainfall** is a major control (in the absence of irrigation) on farming possibilities. The **rainfall regime** largely determines the pattern of the year's work. The **reliability of the rainfall** (*Book 2* p111) influences the farmer's judgement as to what he may safely risk sowing or planting in each successive year.

2 **Length of growing season** – the number of months with a given mean minimum temperature – determines what crops (except under glass) a farmer can hope to harvest. The **diurnal range of temperature**, determining the risk of night frost in the early or late growing season, is a further control, especially with sensitive crops such as coffee or cotton.

3 **Altitude**   Increased altitude limits the farmer's choice because of lowered temperature and wider diurnal range (p60).

4 **Latitude**   Increased latitude (ie distance from the Equator) also brings, on the whole, lower temperatures.

These two factors reinforce each other so that (eg) crops which flourish at 3000m in East Africa will barely grow at 300m in northern England; but the longer hours of daylight in high latitudes do compensate to some extent for the less powerful insolation.

5 **Aspect** (p59) controls the effective degree of insolation.

6 **Slope** affects the farmer's work by (eg) limiting his use of machinery and increasing the risk of soil erosion.

7 **Soil** may (eg) be fertile or infertile; easily drained, or otherwise; quick or slow to warm up in spring.

8 **Pests and diseases**   The prevalence of (eg) tsetse fly or virus crop diseases may make it unprofitable to attempt some types of farming. Preventive measures may be costly and/or ineffective.

Human factors

1 **Efficiency**   The intelligence, health and vigour of the farmer affect the results he can achieve, as do his knowledge and organizing skill. Malnutrition, and the **deficiency diseases** it causes (*Book 2* p149) often stunt mental as well as physical development. Illiteracy is a barrier to learning and understanding new ideas. Those who most need to achieve higher standards in their farming are therefore least likely to do so.

2 **Land-holding systems**   The size of his farm, and whether rented or owned (or shared, as on a Soviet collective or Chinese commune); whether conveniently laid out, or fragmented in widely scattered strips; these and similar factors affect the productivity of farm holdings.

3 **Social and religious customs**   In many countries the diet, and therefore the farmer's activities, is limited by restrictions, eg Hindus cannot eat beef, nor Moslems pork.

4 **Accessibility to markets**   eg New Zealand's sheep-rearing and dairying industries were of minor importance until the development of refrigerator ships made it possible to carry frozen food through the Tropics to Europe.

   The Canadian Prairies (*Book 2* p126) were not producers of wheat until the building of the trans-continental railways and their many branch lines made bulk transport available to every settler.

5 **Market demand**   Farming cannot pay unless the market price is high enough to cover the farmer's costs.

6 **Political controls**   The previous factor may be offset by subsidies from a government which wishes to help particular farmers (eg in difficult hilly areas) to stay in business. Similarly, to ensure supplies in time of war, the British government has for many years subsidized sugar beet production, but only a certain area is subsidized, and individual farmers are allotted a 'quota' of so many hectares which they are not allowed to exceed.

   The 'soil bank' (p125) is a negative method of government control used not only to counteract soil erosion but also to avoid over-production of a particular crop and a consequent slump in price.

7 **Labour supply**   Without help of the right kind, farmers are limited

in scope, eg many British farmers have sold some or all of their dairy cows because they cannot find stockmen willing to work the long hours required.

Types of farming

Easily the most frequent form of general question on farming is about different types. That quoted on p116 is typical, as are the following:

56 *With specific reference to African areas you have studied describe the characteristic features of* (i) shifting agriculture, (ii) pastoral nomadism, (iii) plantation-type agriculture. *In your answer explain the factors which favour each particular type of activity.*   (WEL)

57 (a) *Locate by means of a sketch-map one area important for plantation agriculture.*

   (b) *Write an account of farming in the area you have selected, paying particular attention to the problems of crop production, labour supply and markets.*

   (c) *Describe the benefits gained from plantation farming in the area.*   (AEB)

58 (a) *Describe the differences between cooperative farming of the capitalist type and collective farming of the communist type. Suggest reasons to account for those differences.*

   (b) *Choose one of these types of farming and by reference to an area you have studied, describe the system of farming. To what extent has it been successful?*   (JMB)

59 (a) *On the accompanying world map locate and name one area important for each of four of the following types of agriculture: plantation agriculture; nomadic pastoralism; intensive multi-cropping; tropical extensive grazing. Add a key.*

   (b) *For any two of these types, explain why they have developed.*   (LOND)

Note the repeated call for specific located examples, usually with sketch-maps; and for details of 'factors', 'problems', 'reasons' and explanations. If the syllabus includes a regional section you may have no difficulty in supplying such examples. You must in any case be able to do so and to show what factors (pp116–17) account for the farmer's choice of activity, in respect of each of the following topics.

There is room here for only a bare summary, with indications of some special points that should be brought out in answers. Essential descriptive detail, preferably of named and located examples, must be sought in your textbook.

An increasingly common type of question covers much the same ground as the examples given above, but is based on a photograph of farming activity. You must therefore be familiar with the distinctive appearance of each of the following:

Nomadic pastoralism (or **pastoral nomadism**) Increasingly rare, but still found in some arctic or arid regions (eg) Middle East, North and East Africa, Northern Siberia, Central Asia. Livestock: camels, sheep, goats, cattle, yaks, reindeer or horses, varying with locality. Mainly a primitive form of near-subsistence farming, but in Central Asia (USSR) organized on a commercial basis, the nomadic groups forming part of a **collective** (see p121). *Not* random wandering, but a seasonal progress through a series of grazing areas, none of which could support flocks and herds for long at a time.

Transhumance appears similar to nomadism, but is not. A feature of mountainous countries, in which the settled farmers of lowlands and valley floors transport or drive their cattle and sheep to the high mountain pastures in early summer and down again in winter, thus leaving lower land free for growing fodder crops in summer. The upland farm on p114 is a (very small-scale) example. This type of farming is still common in Alpine and Mediterranean lands, but less so than formerly because few herdsmen will now accept the long separation from village life that was once entailed. In addition, better roads and equipment now make it easier to cut the mountain pastures for hay, and thus to keep the livestock in the valley all the year under more intensive conditions. Transhumance on a large scale and over long distances is practised by ranchers in the Western Cordillera of the USA.

Extensive grazing (**ranching**) of cattle and sheep. Important chiefly in the drier areas of temperate grasslands. The only commercial farming activity of any great value in many tropical grassland areas. Developed after the late nineteenth-century invention of barbed wire, which made fencing practicable even in regions devoid of timber. Never found in areas suited to crop farming. In recent years the introduction of fodder crops suited to dry conditions (eg grain sorghum) or grown under irrigation (eg lucerne) has enabled ranchers to rear more stock on smaller holdings.

Pests, disease and adverse climatic conditions make ranching in the tropics less rewarding than in temperate lands.

Extensive sheep rearing is mainly for wool. Most lamb comes from more intensive farms in moister regions such as New Zealand or Britain.

Dairying requires heavy feeding, constant attention, costly equipment and reliable transport. It is thus an intensive form of pastoralism. Main production is from mild, moist regions (eg Ireland, New Zealand) and from temperate regions with good access to densely-populated urban areas (eg northeastern USA, Denmark, Netherlands).

Intensive livestock rearing varies in degree from (eg) the lowland farm on p114 to the 'factory farming' methods by which most eggs and poultry and much beef and pig meat is now produced indoors in closely confined conditions.

Shifting cultivation: a simple form of communal subsistence farming practised in some tropical forest regions. The 'slash-and-burn / cultivate / move on' technique gives a good return for the labour involved, but only so long as large areas of land are available. This is because each cleared patch needs thirty years or more to recover its fertility. Increased population involves clearing at shorter intervals, with a progressive decline in food production.

Intensive multi-cropping mainly for subsistence, and typical of the more crowded tropical lands (eg China, Japan, Indonesia). Given fertile soil, heavy rainfall, high temperatures and endless labour, two or three grain crops (usually rice) can be grown each year, with vegetables and fruit on any spare ground.

Market gardening or horticulture (**truck farming** in North America): the purely commercial version of multi-cropping. Main products: flowers and salad vegetables. Highly intensive methods, often under glass. Located usually (a) in or near densely-populated urban areas or (b) in climatically favoured areas where early crops (**primeurs**) can be grown (eg Channel Islands, the French Riviera).

Factor (a) was once of supreme importance. Modern transport has given much more emphasis to (b); eg out-of-season lettuce are flown into the London markets from California.

Intensive mixed farming: Livestock, fodder crops and cash crops grown in rotation to maintain fertility and cash income. Typical of northwest Europe and the Middle-West of America, but recent tendency has been to specialize (eg more arable in East Anglia and the Paris Basin; more livestock in the Middle-West).

Irrigation farming Costly in money or labour, or both, and therefore normally used for intensively cultivated, high-value crops. Methods include flooding hill-terraces for rice (southeast Asia); diverting rivers and artesian water (p41), by dams or otherwise, into distribution channels; raising by hand from rivers (eg Egypt) or wells (eg India); and artificial 'rain' sprayed by pumps. Irrigation plays a major role in Mediterranean (summer drought) lands, and is increasingly used in fairly humid regions (p111).

Collective farming includes the **kolkhoz** (collective farms) and **sovkhoz** (State farms) of USSR, and the **communes** of modern China. Found only where a communist government is strong enough to overrule the natural preference of farmers for working independently. Results after sixty years in USSR – disappointing; after thirty years in China – food supplies apparently more secure than under the old system of individual peasant farming.

Cooperative farming   Most farms in northwest Europe are small or medium in size. Many of them belong to voluntary groups which, dealing in bulk, can get better terms for buying machinery, fertilizers, etc, and for selling their produce. Denmark and Eire are leading examples. The principle is spreading to developing countries such as Kenya, where peasants are helped in this way to turn from subsistence to cash farming.

Plantation agriculture dates from the earliest days of European expansion into less-developed and mainly tropical regions such as Latin America, Africa and Southeast Asia. European or American managers and money control large estates, and employ local, low-paid and largely unskilled labour to produce food and raw materials for export to industrialized countries. Typical plantation crops: rubber, sugar, tea, coffee, cotton, bananas. In most such countries there is now a strong trend towards using local management, and even to breaking up the estates into peasant cooperatives.

Extensive grain farming The large-scale, one-crop (**monoculture**), highly-mechanized style of (eg) the North American Prairies or the Ukraine. Low yields per hectare are offset by large areas and efficient bulk handling. Reliance on one completely commercial crop leaves farmers at risk from variable rainfall, summer storms and fluctuating world prices; but often there is little scope for diversifying into other crops because of climatic or marketing limitations.

Farming and climate

In most regions there is a wide variety of farming activities, but really important crops and livestock products always reflect the features of climate which best suit them. Only such major products are listed in the following summary of farming in the various climatic regions (pp84–9):

Equatorial Lowland   Degree of development very varied, eg intensive cultivation in Java contrasting with negligible activity in Amazonia. Not surprisingly, tree crops (often in commercial plantations) are the most distinctive products: coconut, oil palm, cocoa, rubber, bananas. Food crops: rice and maize (especially in Indonesia), yams, cassava.

Equatorial Highland   Almost any activity possible, depending on altitude. Tea, coffee, sugar cane and maize on lower slopes give way to (eg) wheat, potatoes, dairying and sheep from around 2500m upwards.

Tropical Maritime   Much as Equatorial Lowland. Sugar cane also a major crop on all Trade Wind coasts and islands. Coffee, mainly on fairly high ground, especially important in Brazil and Central Ameria.

Tropical Continental   Tea, cotton, citrus fruit, tobacco, groundnuts, sugar cane, maize, millet – according to soil quality and total mean rainfall. Wheat sometimes grown in cool season. Extensive cattle ranching in drier districts. Irrigation usually necessary for full productivity.

Tropical Monsoon   Rice, sugar cane, tea, coconuts (on coasts), cotton, maize and millet (in drier districts, especially of northern India and Pakistan), wheat and beans (cool season crops in northern India and Pakistan, usually with irrigation).

Hot Desert   With practically continuous strong sunshine, almost anything will grow where oasis or irrigation water is available. Tropical crops in hot season, temperate crops in cool season (eg intensive peasant farming in Egypt, intensive large-scale commercial production of lettuce and other salad crops in Arizona, USA).

Mediterranean   Summer drought results in very distinctive traditional farming pattern. Winter crops: wheat, barley and beans, harvested in early summer. Summer crops: grapes and olives (for wine and oil) and maize (where water available) harvested in autumn; sheep and goats maintained by transhumance (p119).

Modern developments based largely on irrigation. Intensive horticulture (eg French/Italian Riviera, Cyprus); rice (eastern Spain, southern France); cotton (Turkey); citrus fruit (Sicily, Israel). In the Central Valley of California, mass production of all such crops by large-scale 'agribusiness'.

Gulf or China   Because the land masses are so much larger, Northern Hemisphere examples have a much less equable climate than in the Southern Hemisphere. History and population density account for other marked differences (eg development much more intensive in Japan and Central China).

Rice, maize, wheat, soya beans, linseed, sugar cane, cotton, tea, tobacco are typical crops. Cattle important in southeast USA and in southern continents, pigs in China.

Cool Temperate Oceanic   Covers perhaps the greatest contrasts of all. Northwest Europe intensively developed; British Columbia, northwest USA, Tasmania and New Zealand, fairly well-developed; southern Chile, almost undeveloped.

Climate typically cool and moist, ideal for dairying and deciduous orchard fruit (especially apples). Inland areas of northwest Europe (eg East Anglia, Paris Basin, Rhineland) have summers well-suited to wheat and root crops. Population pressure has made northwest Europe the outstanding example of mixed farming (p120).

Cool Temperate Eastern Margin   Scope of farming generally limited by cold winters. In the more favoured areas (eg south Ontario) products similar to those of previous type.

Continental (Interior temperate grasslands)   Much smaller in extent in Southern Hemisphere because land masses smaller. The world's great stock-rearing and grain-farming areas, mainly on large-scale extensive basis because unreliable rainfall (periodic cycles of drought years) makes it hard for small farmers to survive. A more mixed style of farming is growing up around urban areas and where irrigation is possible.

Cold Temperate   Some pasture and potatoes in favoured spots along southern fringe (eg eastern Canada, Finland) but nowhere of importance.

Arctic   No farming except for experimental research stations in northern Canada and northern Siberia.

Soil erosion

The quotation in question 60 below is so true that no summary of world farming can ignore this topic. Three points must be grasped before it can be understood in detail:

1 **soil erosion is a natural process**, forming part of the cycle of
   denudation (p34) and is in continuous progress.
2 **soil erosion is accelerated by bad farming**   In some cases
   careless forestry, change of climate and overpopulation by wild
   animals are other factors, but the major factor is undoubtedly the
   attempt by Man, consciously or otherwise, to overwork the soil.
3 **soil erosion must be prevented** as far as is humanly possible,

because the survival of a rapidly increasing world population depends on wise use of this thin and easily-destroyed surface layer.

Here are three questions from very different syllabuses:

60 *'Soil erosion is one of the most pressing problems threatening Mankind.'*
Elaborate this statement by reference to specific areas. (OX)
61 (a) *'Soil erosion is often the product of careless cultivation and overgrazing.' Explain this statement.*
   (b) *Name two regions which have been affected by soil erosion, and for each region describe the methods that are being used in its control.* (AEB)
62 *Contour ploughing, hill slope terracing, reafforestation and the planting of shelter belts are all methods of combating soil erosion. Briefly explain each of the four methods and show how these techniques help to prevent soil erosion.* (LOND)

Despite the very different wording of these questions, in each case the answer must describe causes, results and counter-measures, with illustrations from both developed and Third World countries. Questions on soil erosion are so frequent that you should prepare answers, at least in outline, to all the above, making sure that your reading has provided enough detail to help you to expand the following points.

Causes and results
1 deforestation on hill slopes followed by cultivation, leaving soil open to heavy rain. Even on gentle slopes, runoff cuts channels which soon become **gulleys**, and bare rock is quickly exposed. Land becomes useless; farmer abandons it and moves to clear more trees, making matters worse: eg Appalachian Mountains, USA, in 18th–19th centuries; northern China.
2 **ploughing grassland** in regions of variable rainfall. The soil of natural grasslands is covered by a thick mat of vegetation which protects it by soaking up the rain. Every few decades, rainfall in several successive years falls far short of average. Crops fail, and wind erosion removes the finer particles of the exposed soil. Unless interrupted, the process continues until a 'Dust Bowl' is formed: eg the High Plains of USA; the 'Virgin Lands' of western Siberia.
3 **overstocking of grazing animals**, especially by primitive peoples who value numbers of cattle rather than quality, eg East Africa. 'Over-grazed' pasture results in **sheet erosion** when storm water runs over the bare surface. Animals also make tracks which easily develop into gulleys.

Prevention and cure

1 **reafforestation** takes land out of cultivation and (on slopes) reduces runoff. On level ground, shelter belts of trees form wind breaks and reduce evaporation from the soil, thus lessening frequency of dust storms.

2 **blocking gulleys** with brushwood to trap soil and stones.

3 **planting cover crops** of creeping plants which grow more easily than grass and protect any remaining soil. Land unsuited to cultivation may thus be restored for use as grazing.

4 **contour ploughing**, across slopes rather than up and down, retains moisture and minimizes runoff. So does –

5 **terracing** on steep slopes. Possible only where labour is very cheap and population pressure very great, as in southeast Asia.

6 **strip cropping**   Alternate strips of two or more different crops, sown at right angles to the prevailing wind, leave no large continuous area of soil bare at any time.

7 **'trash farming'**   Stubble and straw are not ploughed into the soil, but left as a protective mat on the surface.

9 **'soil bank'**   In the USA some farmers are actually paid *not* to cultivate land especially vulnerable to soil erosion.

8 **education** has (eg) persuaded some African farmers to appreciate quality rather than numbers of livestock, and also to control the movements of their animals by fencing and by improving water supplies, feeding arrangements, etc.

8 Settlement

Geography is lagrely concerned with where people live, and why.

In recent years phrases like 'urban studies', with various associated technical terms, have entered school syllabuses and textbooks. The new approach is merely a more scientific and systematic way of considering the places, whether town or country, in which we spend our lives. For example:

63 (a) *Describe the sites, positions and main functions of villages and other rural settlements in a small area of which you have made a special study.*
   (b) *Give an account of the physical and economic factors which influence the siting and distribution of rural settlements in general.* (O & C)
64 *By means of named examples, explain what you understand by three of the following: (i) urban hierarchies; (ii) functional zones of towns; (iii) conurbations; (iv) gap towns; (v) New Towns.* (LOND)

Though one is about rural and the other about urban settlement, the questions are linked. The information to answer them falls into three sections: (a) how and why settlements begin; (b) why some grow faster than others; (c) the various forms that settlements take as they grow.

In Britain and elsewhere broad stretches of countryside are still dotted with separate farms, reminding us that our remote ancestors were almost all farmers. Soil, ground space and water were essentials of their lives. Where water was widely available from streams or wells, or where (eg in barren highland areas) only scattered patches of land could support a family group, **dispersed settlement** was the rule. Yet many then lived, and most of us live now, in villages or towns; this is **nucleated settlement.** Why did these settlements develop in some places rather than in others? Why has one village remained much the same in size for hundreds of years while another, very similar in its origins, has grown many times larger?

Settlement sites

Almost all towns have developed from former villages; thus we can best start by looking at village **sites** – the particular spots which one or more family groups chose for their homes. Their choice was based on simple day-to-day needs.

1 **Wet-point sites,** by streams or lakes, offered a convenient water supply. Particularly notable are various series of **spring-line villages** along the scarp foot of (eg) the Chilterns and Cotswolds (diagram p39).

2 **Dry-point sites** Settlements on firm ground, close to undrained marshes, were convenient both for tree-felling and farming (above flood level) and also for fishing, wild fowling and the cutting of reeds and peat. East Anglia has many such 'fen-line' villages.

3 **Defensive sites** were especially important in some districts. Hill tops, river meanders (see p128) or islands (in rivers, lakes or marshes) gave security by their seclusion.

4 **Crossing points** of rivers or of natural trackways were convenient for local use, and gave a chance of trade with passing travellers.

5 **Gaps** in hills had similar advantages.

Find examples of these typical sites from a textbook or from first-hand knowledge. Note that many sites combine two or more of the advantages listed.

SOME TYPICAL VILLAGE SHAPES

Early settlements took various forms, often still recognisable, such as (a) **linear** or **street** villages, and (b) **nucleated villages** (i) round a village green or market place or (ii) at a crossroads.

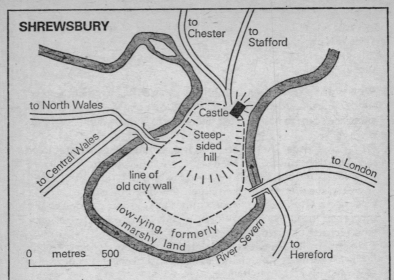

Site Steep-sided hill, almost completely enclosed by a meander.
Location On border between Welsh highlands and English lowlands, in an area of fertile soil. First a military base for English rule over Wales, later a centre of trade and transport.

Location

Of every hundred villages, only a few grew into towns. Some grew because they occupied good defensive sites (*see opposite*) with military garrisons which gave merchants the confidence to settle there, thus encouraging trade and further growth of population. But defence against *whom?* – and trade in *what?*

The answer lay in the developing town's **location** (or **position**) in relation to the wider area with which its people were, at any point in history, in contact – its **hinterland**. Defence was much more important in some districts, such as the Scottish and Welsh borders, than in others. Trade was mainly in farm products; a location in a fertile area, or where two types of farming (eg highland and lowland) lay close together and thus stimulated trade in different products such as wool and grain, was a major stimulus to growth. Almost all early towns were principally market centres. Industrial towns are a relatively new development, but they too have grown up as a result of their location in respect of (eg) mineral deposits or transport facilities.

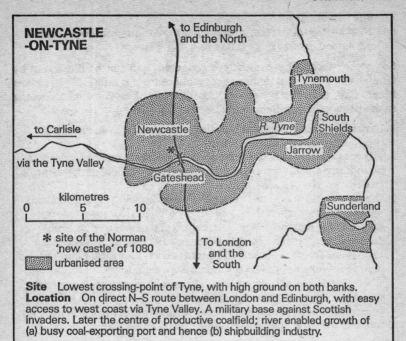

NEWCASTLE-ON-TYNE

to Edinburgh and the North

Tynemouth

to Carlisle

Newcastle

R. Tyne

South Shields

via the Tyne Valley

Jarrow

Gateshead

kilometres

0   5   10

* site of the Norman 'new castle' of 1080

urbanised area

To London and the South

Sunderland

Site   Lowest crossing-point of Tyne, with high ground on both banks.
Location   On direct N–S route between London and Edinburgh, with easy access to west coast via Tyne Valley. A military base against Scottish invaders. Later the centre of productive coalfield; river enabled growth of (a) busy coal-exporting port and hence (b) shipbuilding industry.

Questions are often set to test understanding of the factors of location; eg:

65 *With the aid of annotated sketch-maps, describe the position and importance of* two *of the following:* (five major towns of the British Isles).   (LOND)

Simple sketch-maps with concise 'labels' are by no means the whole answer to such a question, but they are more than half the answer. The examples opposite may be taken as models for summaries of revision reading. For examination purposes one paragraph explaining and amplifying the map, and one more describing the town's present importance, would be enough for each half question.

Sometimes a sketch-map or diagram is provided, and the candidate is asked to comment on the advantages of the location it illustrates. Such questions usually concentrate on **accessibility**, a major factor in town growth as in mining (p98). Road, rail, air, inland water and sea access may all have to be considered.

Urban hierarchy

66 *What are the factors that contribute to the variation in size of towns in*
one named *country ?* (LOND)

Some such factors have already been noted, and can be illustrated by
familiar examples; but modern geographers are also interested in **urban
hierarchy**, ie in the systematic classification of settlements according
to size or stage of development. They distinguish:

1 **hamlets** – small groups of buildings, separate from any larger
community but not independent.
2 **villages** – larger rural settlements with a church, one or more shops
including probably a sub-post office, perhaps a school, etc; ie centres,
but only to a limited degree.
3 **towns** – settlements large enough to provide facilities for living and
working quite distinct from a rural way of life. Most towns are not
only **service centres** (shopping, banking, transport, education,
entertainment, etc) for an extensive hinterland, but have also some
specialized functions (p132). The term **city** is now rather loosely
used in reference to any very large or important town.
    Any service centre, whether village or town, is termed a **central
place** in relation to its own hinterland.
4 **conurbations** are groups of towns, originally separate, which have
expanded to form a more-or-less continuous built-up area.

Other things being equal (which is not always so) there is a noticeable
tendency for settlements to form a pattern in which this hierarchy of
size and function is clearly visible. The diagram opposite should be kept
in mind when answering questions similar to the previous one or to
those on p126; or to:

67 (a) *Describe the* pattern *of settlement shown on the map* [of part of
East Anglia].
   (b) *Describe and account for the different functions of a* regional *centre
as shown on the map.* (WEL)

The ideal conditions of the diagram come fairly close to reality in East
Norfolk, a generally level, fertile and well-watered area colonized over a
thousand years ago by Anglo-Saxon settlers, and for a long period one
of the most densely-populated parts of Britain.

Using an atlas or motoring map of East Anglia, mark on a simple
sketch-map the towns mentioned below.

Norwich (population *c* 180 000) is much the largest town in the region;
the trading, commercial and financial centre of a wide hinterland; a

THEORETICAL PATTERN OF SETTLEMENT HIERARCHY

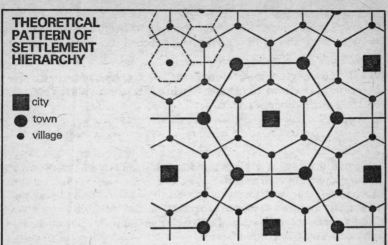

■ city
● town
• village

It can be shown that if equal-sized groups of farmer-settlers worked equally hard in a level countryside of uniform fertility, the settlement pattern should eventually be that suggested in this diagram; ie a network of villages, each cultivating hexagonal hinterlands (as shown at top left). Simple measurement also suggests that the centre village of each cluster of villages is the most accessible and therefore the most likely to grow into a market town; and that the centre town of each cluster of towns is the most likely to grow into a city offering major services to a wide hinterland.

In real life, of course, development is never quite so regular.

cathedral and university city; an industrial town and a major **transport node** (see map p135). Within a radius of 65km round Norwich no town has over 10 000 inhabitants except for *Great Yarmouth* (*c* 62 000), which has long had a separate function as a seaport; and only five other towns have more than 4 500 population: *North Walsham, East Dereham, Wymondham, Beccles* and *Bungay*. Each of these market towns is a service centre, in greater or less degree, for a ring of large and small villages.

Notice from your map that Beccles and Bungay lie close together in the fertile farming valley of the River Waveney (once a busy water-transport route). Poor accessibility has limited the growth of settlements in the Norfolk Broads; hence the wide gap between North Walsham and Great Yarmouth. Allowing for these special conditions, the 'hexagon' pattern is quite recognizable.

Urban functions

All towns are service centres, but many, probably most, have developed by performing special functions such as those listed below. Questions on this topic are fairly common:

67 (a) *Name* one *example of* three *of the following types of town:* a major industrial town; a market town in a rural area; a port; a New Town; a holiday resort.

(b) *For* each *of your named towns, describe with the aid of a sketch-map the factors which influenced its development for that function.*   (JMB)

Such questions are easily answered, given a general knowledge of the selected examples. (Nearly all towns, of course, perform several functions; check the list below with reference to any town you know well.) The main factors – a nearby coalfield, a natural harbour, etc – are usually obvious; and **accessibility**, either natural or man-made, is almost always an important factor.

Towns may function as:
commercial centres specializing in banking, insurance and international trade: eg the City of London; Zurich; New York.
administrative centres – any capital city or 'county town'; but some sites were selected (eg Westminster) and some towns deliberately planned (eg Canberra, Australia, or Brasilia, Brazil) as centres of government.
industrial (manufacturing) towns, usually with one major and various minor industries: eg Northampton (footwear); Omaha, USA (meat packing); Lyon, France (silks).
residential or 'dormitory' towns within commuting distance of a major centre: eg Amersham, Bucks; Wallasey, Merseyside.
'New Towns' planned and built as self-contained communities to absorb 'overspill' population from congested conurbations: eg Stevenage, Herts; Cumbernauld, Strathclyde.
transport centres (including seaports) where routes cross, or where transport modes meet: eg Crewe (railway junction and repair centre); San Francisco (ocean port); Calais (ferry port).
holiday towns or tourist centres: eg Scarborough; Stratford-on-Avon; Niagara Falls, USA; St Moritz, Switzerland.
educational centres: ancient university towns and cultural centres: eg Cambridge; New Haven, USA; Heidelberg, West Germany.
religious centres of church organizations (eg Canterbury; Salt Lake USA) or of pilgrimage (eg Mecca; Lourdes).
mining towns: eg Barnsley. S. Yorks (coal); Sudbury, Ontario (nickel and copper); Kiruna, Sweden (iron).
fishing ports with associated canning, freezing and other processing industries: eg Hull; Seattle, USA; Bergen, Norway.

Urban structure

Urban structure and functional zones These are two more technical terms now in common use. They refer to the pattern which in almost any town can be identified more or less (but never exactly) as in the model below. You may be asked to describe and discuss these zones; to recognize them on a large-scale map or from an air photograph; or to interpret similar information supplied by an **urban transect** (a bar diagram divided to show a cross-section of the zones, from the centre outwards).

FUNCTIONAL ZONES IN A MODERN CITY

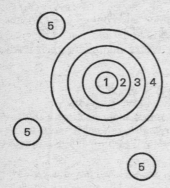

1 The core. Historical town centre. Contains the C.B.D.
2 Older larger houses decaying into slums. Contains some small industries.
3 Heavy industrial zone often mixed with terraced housing.
4 Post-1918 residential area, housing estates. Some light industries.
5 Commuter 'villages'.

This diagram is taken from an OS map question based on Southampton (*O & C*). Other models may be different and perhaps more detailed, but most agree in showing:
1 the **Central Business District (CBD)** marked by high-rise office blocks, department stores, large banks, town hall, market place, etc.
2 an inner ring (*2 and 3 above*) of older, usually nineteenth-century mixed industrial-residential property, probably 'run down' if not already cleared and redeveloped. This is the **zone of urban renewal**.
3 outer rings of twentieth-century council estates or private housing, with some modern industrial estates (usually adjacent to a ring road or bypass) and 'mini-CBD' shopping and service centres.
4 suburbs, often of expensive houses, with plenty of open spaces; or an actual **green belt** of open land, restricting development between **3** and surrounding settlements which have probably become **commuter villages** largely occupied by city workers.

RENT BIDS AND RENT GRADIENTS

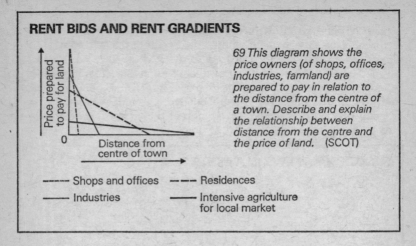

69 This diagram shows the price owners (of shops, offices, industries, farmland) are prepared to pay in relation to the distance from the centre of a town. Describe and explain the relationship between distance from the centre and the price of land. (SCOT)

----- Shops and offices   --- Residences

——— Industries   ——— Intensive agriculture for local market

Rent bids Why does the CBD of any town, large or small, contain most of its tall buildings ? The answer lies in this diagram.

For some purposes central sites are much more profitable than sites further out, and so there is a great demand for them. This in turn enables landowners to spend large sums on tall buildings and still make a profit by selling or renting them.

The diagram shows that some users (*which ?*) will pay much more for a central site than for one even a little way out. Others would pay a little more for a central site, but their 'rent bid' is not high enough to secure it.

Study the graphs carefully and note how they explain the zones of the previous model. State in simple terms why the **rent gradient** – the relation of rent bid to distance from centre – is much steeper for some users than others. Suggest why, since 1945, many market gardeners have sold suburban land and moved further out.

Wherever possible, check textbook ideas against your own experience. This will help you to deal convincingly with questions such as :

68 *For a town in the British Isles of which you have made a special study, write on* two *of the following :*
   (a) *factors influencing its growth.*
   (b) *the characteristics and problems associated with its CBD;*
   (c) *the location of its industrial and residential areas;*
   (d) *its traffic problems and attempted solutions.* (O & C)

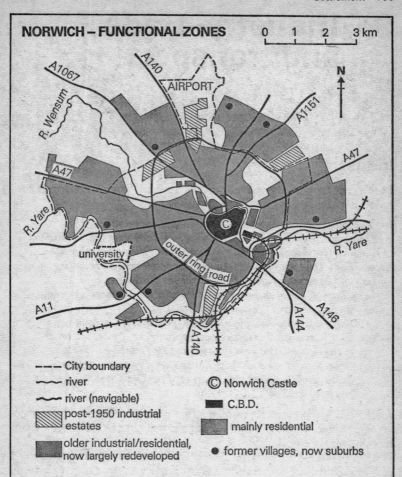

NORWICH – FUNCTIONAL ZONES

0   1   2   3 km

Legend:

- – – – City boundary
- ⌒ river
- ⌒ river (navigable)
- ▨ post-1950 industrial estates
- ▓ older industrial/residential, now largely redeveloped
- Ⓒ Norwich Castle
- ▬ C.B.D.
- ▓ mainly residential
- ● former villages, now suburbs

Central Norwich, already badly 'run down' after a long period of industrial and agricultural depression, suffered severe bombing in World War 2. Since 1950 there has been extensive renewal of the central areas as well as rapid growth outwards. *Compare this map with the diagram of Southampton on p133. What similarities do you notice? What transport modes – road, rail, sea, air – serve (a) the older and (b) the new industrial areas?*

What natural feature, in a generally level countryside, has imposed a southern limit to 'urban sprawl'?

Note the position of Norwich Castle in relation to the river, and compare it with the map of Shrewsbury (p128).

9 Industry, trade and transport

Industry

In the chapter heading above, this word means 'manufacturing industry', but it often means simply 'occupation' as in:

70 *The following are important occupations in one country of the Developed World: (i) tyre manufacture (ii) lumbering (iii) aluminium smelting (iv) banking (v) electronic calculator assembly (vi) fish processing (vii) zinc mining (viii) hotel management and catering (ix) soft drink manufacture (x) natural gas production.*
   (a) *Classify each of these occupations under the headings 'Primary', 'Secondary' and 'Tertiary' industries.*
   (b) *Suggest three other likely tertiary industries in the country.*
   (c) *Briefly explain why tertiary occupations are of more importance in the Developed World than in the Less Developed World.*
   (d) *What factors affect the location and development of tertiary industries in a named area or areas of the Developed World that you have studied?*   (LOND)

After reading the notes opposite, attempt parts (a), (b) and (c). Answers to (a) are given below. If you made any mistakes, try to account for them by re-reading the notes.

As to (d); service industries develop, like any other, where there is a demand for them, ie where there is the largest number of people to be served. Thus the major factor in the location of most tertiary industries is the presence of a dense population; and the major factor in their development is the average prosperity of that population. A big town has more shops than a village, and a prosperous big town has more 'high class' (ie expensive) shops.

Answers

Primary: (ii) (vii) (x)   Secondary: (i) (iii) (v) (vi) (ix)   Tertiary: (iv) (viii)

Many towns have an above-average proportion of one type of tertiary worker: capital cities in particular, but also (eg) garrison or university towns, cathedral cities and tourist resorts. Remember, though, that all 'central places' (p131) are service centres. Even a busy factory city has usually more tertiary than secondary workers.

With these points in mind, select named examples for an answer to (d).

Classes of industry

1 primary industries are the extractive industries (p92) and farming. All are concerned with making available the Earth's natural resources.
2 secondary industries, normally carried on in factories, convert primary products into more useful forms; in other words they process raw materials into manufactured goods. Note, however, that the 'manufactured goods' of one industry, eg sheet steel, may be the 'raw materials' of another secondary industry, eg vehicle manufacture.
3 tertiary industries are otherwise known as 'non-productive' or 'service' occupations. They include professional and office workers and those in trade, transport, defence, entertainment, etc.

UNITED STATES

INDIA

These diagrams show the proportion of the working population in each occupation-group in one country of the developed world and one country of the less developed ('Third') world.

In developed countries farming and other primary industries are as highly mechanized as manufacturing, so that productivity per worker is high. Such a specialized system produces (i) a need for great numbers of workers in (eg) transport, trade, education and government, and (ii) the wealth to support these 'non-productive' workers and also others (eg doctors, hotel-keepers, entertainers) in numbers that only a wealthy community can afford.

In Third World countries the near-subsistence cultivators, who make up the bulk of the population, have so little cash income that the *effective* demand for 'services' is very small, badly though some of those workers, such as doctors and teachers, may be needed.

Factors in the location of industry

Why are some places noted for a particular industry? Why does an industry established in a particular place sometimes lose ground to competitors elsewhere? These are important topics in any regional study, and are also frequent subjects for general questions, such as:

71 (a) *Choose two geographical factors in the location of industry and describe their effects on specific industries.*

   (b) *Give actual examples of how* non-geographical *factors have influenced the location of industries.* (SCOT half-question)

72 *With special reference to* one *named example, explain the advantages of coastal sites for modern steelworks.* (SUJB)

73 *For any* one named *country, explain the differences in the factors affecting the location of the steel industry and that of the automobile industry.* (LOND)

Other industries often made the subject of such questions are oil refining and the manufacture of textiles and chemicals. The same principles apply to all. After reading the list below, decide what factors might affect the location of each of the primary and secondary industries named in the question on p136. (There are no *certain* answers to most such problems, but the major factor is usually fairly obvious.) Using these pages, *Book 2*, and your textbook, prepare full answers for *two* countries to Q73 above.

The principal geographical factors relate to:

1 **raw materials** Are these very bulky in relation to the value of the product? If so, a location near the supply is desirable, eg (a) brick making on the Oxford Clay outcrop near Bedford or Peterborough, or (b) wood-pulp manufacture in the taiga of Eastern Canada.

2 **power** Some industries require large supplies of cheap power, eg (a) aluminium refining in the Pacific northwest of the United States, using HEP from the Columbia River, or (b) (once more) wood-pulp in eastern Canada, using local HEP.

3 **labour** Some industries depend on a plentiful supply of cheap labour (eg tea growing in Sri Lanka). Others require a high proportion of skilled workers and must therefore locate in areas of high educational standards (eg electronics in New England).

4 **markets** Who will buy the finished goods? If the industry's operations are not so space-consuming as to make the cost of land too high, a densely-populated area is a desirable location. Luxury goods and perishables in particular feel 'the pull of the market' (eg fashionable clothes in most capital cities, bread in any large town).

5 transport   Very few locations cover all of factors 1–4. How accessible are the missing ones? Lack of cheap transport held up development until the canals and railways of the 18th–19th centuries made the Industrial Revolution possible. Recent advances in bulk transport (p142) have still further reduced the **friction of distance** (p143) which once limited industrial location very severely. The importance of accessibility is shown by the new factories that spring up near so many motorway intersections.

6 geographical inertia (sometimes called **industrial momentum**) An industry, once firmly established, tends to remain where it is even if other locations become more attractive. The best example is the steel industry (overleaf).

Human or non-geographical factors include:

1 conservation   Many industries need huge supplies of water (eg oil refineries, power stations, dye-works) and the resulting **effluent** or waste heat may affect and pollute rivers further downstream. Air pollution cannot always be avoided. The law, backed by growing public opinion, now restricts such developments in many locations which would otherwise be satisfactory. (See Europort overleaf.)

2 government policy   In what is thought to be the national interest, a firm may be told where it may or may not expand; eg Ford's, barred in the 1960s from building a new factory in the prosperous, busy Midlands, and offered tax inducements to build it instead at Halewood, on Merseyside, to help relieve unemployment.

In answering questions on industrial location, remember that any firm's decision is almost certainly a compromise between two or more of these factors. Only by results can it be judged whether the choice was a good one. Furthermore, factors change in value for better or worse; obvious examples might be the closure of a railway line or the extension of a motorway, thus impairing or improving accessibility. The most striking change of recent years, perhaps, has been the steel industry's world-wide tendency to develop at 'tidewater' locations (Q72 opposite) in order to profit from the advances in bulk transport mentioned above. Northwest Europe shows some excellent examples of this trend and of the counter-effect of geographical inertia.

Factors in the location of the steel industry

As recently as 1850, up to ten tonnes of coking coal were needed to produce one tonne of iron. 'Ore moves to coal' was the general rule, for obvious reasons, even though the ore might contain less than 40 per cent iron. Ore is now usually **beneficiated** – crushed and partly refined – at the mine, and coal is cleaned and graded in a similar way; and modern furnaces require only half a tonne of coal per ton of iron. The cost of transporting raw materials is thus a much smaller factor in determining the location of a new steelworks. It is still a major factor, nonetheless, and there is a strong preference for 'tidewater' sites accessible to modern ships which can carry ore or coal at a quarter the cost of river barges and at a twelfth of the cost of railways.

On the other hand, the enormous cost of the fixed plant involved in a big steelworks and the large numbers of skilled men employed means that geographical inertia is particularly strong in the steel industry. Steel firms try very hard to adapt old locations to new conditions rather than abandon them. Factors reinforcing this inertia are the engineering industries that usually develop in a steelmaking centre, providing a ready local market and also a supply of scrap metal. (A modern steelworks uses as much scrap as ore.)

The result is illustrated in the map and diagrams. (If Western Europe is included in your syllabus you must know much more detail than is included in the following summary. Note particularly the part played by navigable inland waterways.)

A Ruhr coalfield Europe's leading centre of heavy industry for the past century. Iron/steelmaking originally based on local coal and ore. Ore now imported from Luxembourg/Lorraine and from various overseas sources. Huge engineering industries.

B Franco-Belgian coalfield Long-established iron/steel industry originally based on local coal and nearby (Ardennes) ore. Ore now imported from Luxembourg/Lorraine and overseas. Some coal also from overseas (local coal now scarce and dear). Very important engineering industries.

C Luxembourg/Lorraine iron orefield Among the world's major steelmaking areas. 'Lean' (low in iron content) ores, once abundant and cheaply mined, now approaching end of profitable life. Supplies now supplemented by overseas imports via Rotterdam. Coal imported from Ruhr and overseas.

D Saar coalfield Local coal (supplemented from Ruhr), Lorraine and overseas ore. An important producer.

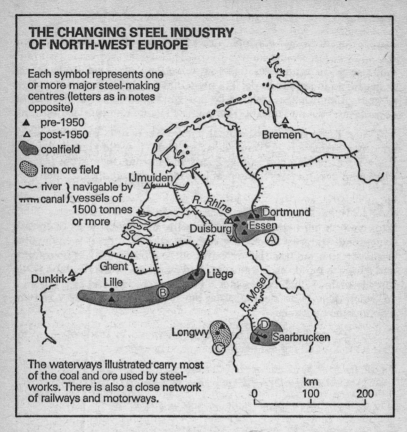

THE CHANGING STEEL INDUSTRY OF NORTH-WEST EUROPE

Each symbol represents one or more major steel-making centres (letters as in notes opposite)

▲ pre-1950
△ post-1950
coalfield
iron ore field
∼ river ⎱ navigable by
⊓⊓⊓ canal ⎰ vessels of
1500 tonnes or more

Bremen

IJmuiden

R. Rhine

Duisburg   Essen   Dortmund
A

Ghent   Liège
Dunkirk   Lille
B   R. Mosel

Longwy   D
C   Saarbrucken

The waterways illustrated carry most of the coal and ore used by steel-works. There is also a close network of railways and motorways.

km
0   100   200

While expanding production in the older locations (marked on map above) the authorities controlling the industry (The European Coal and Steel Community, established in 1952) have also looked for entirely new locations. These 'greenfield sites' can be planned entirely on modern lines without having to adapt to existing buildings, roads, etc. The sites chosen, as the map shows, are usually on tidewater, where they can reap the full benefit of cheap bulk ocean transport.

The star marks a site at Rotterdam/Europort which was ideal in every way except that local opinion objected to having any more 'dirty' industry in an area already badly polluted by the world's biggest assembly of oil refineries. The factor of conservation thus overruled all the others.

Trade

Direct questions on this topic are fairly rare. Three Boards (LOND, OX, WEL) require some knowledge of Britain's foreign trade. Another (SCOT) expects candidates to know something of world trade in the major foods and raw materials (as suggested on p113). These are matters of general knowledge, covered by any good textbook. Questions often require candidates to interpret simple 'pie' graphs and bar diagrams.

Trade, internal or international, enters frequently into other topics such as settlement (Ch.8) and transport, and it is well to remember that the work of buying and selling goods and moving them from place to place employs almost as many people as making or producing them.

Transport

This topic is inextricably bound up with all other aspects of human geography. Industry (including commercial agriculture) is impossible without trade, and trade is impossible without transport. Yet no country can afford to build roads, railways, ports, etc, for which the need is not already plain. Which comes first? This is a 'chicken and egg' question to which there is no clear answer; but it enters into a wide variety of examination questions.

Some are straightforward and can be answered by study of an up-to-date textbook and regular reading of a good newspaper.

74 *Write an essay on* one *of the following:*
  Modern developments in ocean transport; pipelines.   (LOND)

The first of these subjects calls for a good paragraph on each of: giant oil tankers (now carrying over half of *all* shipping cargo); other 'bulk carriers' (mainly of coal and iron ore); the decline of long-distance passenger traffic; containerization; changes in port structure. The second requires knowledge of the advantages and disadvantages of pipelines, of their importance to 'offshore' oil and gas installations and of the variety of substances now transported in this way.

All such answers must, of course, be illustrated with named examples, preferably in sketch-map form. This requirement is usually made quite clear:

75 (a) *The growth in the size of ocean-going vessels has resulted in the construction of docks in deeper water areas and the abandonment of some shallower inland docks. Name* one *port where this has happened and describe the changes that have occurred.*

*(b) In the past 25 years many kilometres of motorway have been built.
Write a reasoned geographical account of the benefits and problems
created by motorway development in any one region or
country.*   (AEB)

76 *Describe and account for the economic importance to a major industrial
region of one of the following:
(a) inland waterways; (b) road and rail networks; (c) oil and gas
pipelines.*   (O & C)

For 75(a) either London, Glasgow or Rotterdam/Europoort provides a
good example. 75(b) could well be answered with reference to England,
West Germany or Italy. The Ruhr is perhaps the best example for each
part of 76; but a good way of revising the geography of any such region
would be to answer the question in respect of each of these **transport
modes.**

Look carefully at any mention of 'networks':

77 *Write an essay on one of the following:
(a) road networks; (b) railway networks; (c) internal air transport.*
(LOND)

78 *Examine a map in your atlas of either Canada or Australia.
(a) On a sketch-map show an area where the railway network is well
established and one where it is poorly developed.
(b) Referring to both physical and human factors, explain why each
area has its particular network.*   (SUJB)

In such cases a general description (with examples) may be adequate,
but a really good answer demands some understanding of network
theory including **nodes, links, topological diagrams** and **connec-
tivity** (or **Beta**) **indices.** Find out without delay whether your syllabus
requires this knowledge.

From a geographical point of view, any question about transport is
concerned with **friction of distance** (p139) – the rather obvious fact
that *on the whole* places far apart are not so well located for communicat-
ing and trading with each other as places close together. Every technical
advance that makes transport cheaper, faster or easier reduces this
friction and makes natural resources and manufactured goods more
widely available, because they are more easily accessible; eg iron ore
and coal (p98) or butter and meat (p117).

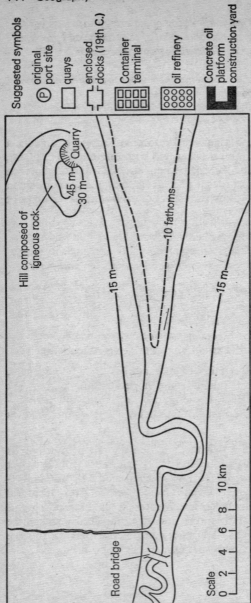

Suggested symbols

Ⓟ original port site

☐ quays

enclosed docks (19th C.)

Container terminal

oil refinery

Concrete oil platform construction yard

Hill composed of igneous rock.

45 m   Quarry
30 m

15 m

10 fathoms

15 m

Road bridge

Scale
0 2 4 6 8 10 km

79 (a) *Study this framework of an estuarine port model. Complete it by indicating the most likely location for the following features: original port site; quays; enclosed docks (19th C.); container terminal; oil refinery; concrete oil platform construction yard. (Use suitable symbols and a key.)*

(b) *Compare this model with a named Scottish port known to you.* (SCOT)

Note This was a half-question. The other parts were applications of the same principles to sketch-maps of past and possible future development on the Clyde.

Suitable sites are suggested opposite. *They are not the only possible sites.* Copy the model and add the suggested symbols as in the notes *or* in locations of your own choice. Justify these in writing.

Changes in the structure of a port

The question quoted opposite applies general principles to a particular example. You may notice a resemblance between the model and the Thames from London to the sea (it is not, of course, an actual map). Taking the required features in printed order, which is the date order in which they might have developed:

Original port site   The meanders indicate a broad flood plain, once probably marshy. The run of the 15-metre contours suggests that the site of the bridge has been a crossing-point from earliest times. The port could not, therefore, develop further upstream, since the **lowest bridging point** was also the **head of navigation,** even for small vessels. These could moor in the mouth of the small tributary just below the bridge. Hull, Liverpool and many other great ports originated from tiny anchorages of this kind.

Quays   As the port develops and ships grow larger, quays are built for more efficient cargo handling, probably on both banks just seaward of the bridge, access to which is important for land transport in either direction.

Enclosed docks (19th century)   Ships are by now much larger and cannot conveniently sail up the busy, winding river. The loop of the meander is formed of easily excavated alluvium. (See any map of the Isle of Dogs in the Thames.)

Container terminal   By the 1960s ships are again much larger and time is lost in manoeuvring them in the narrow channel. A container port needs a broad area of level land for stacking and moving the containers. A site on the south bank near the head of the 10-fathom depth will not be too far from the city which by now has grown up near the bridge.

Oil refinery   Giant tankers need deep water and plenty of turning space. The refinery requires a very large area of level land, close to the shore but as far as possible from built-up areas. The south bank, well downstream from the container terminal, will be a good site.

Concrete oil platform construction yard   Crushed stone ('aggregate') for making concrete can be obtained from the quarry, which is close to deep water, needed for floating the finished platforms. An area between quarry and shore, excavated and perhaps built out into the water, will be the best site.

10 Ordnance Survey maps

Map reading

Almost every O level syllabus requires the study of Ordnance Survey 1:25 000 and 1:50 000 maps. You must be fully familiar with both series. It will be helpful, also, to work through a book based on OS map extracts matched against air photos illustrating different types of British scenery (see p11).

Conventional signs

Nothing, however, can replace the actual learning of the **conventional signs** used in each series. In this respect there are some important differences between the two scales.

For each, carefully distinguish the various forms of broken and dotted line. These include parish and county boundaries, pipelines, power lines and footpaths. Find examples on a map sheet and learn to recognize the differences. Note that a footpath may or may not be a public right of way, and that the 1:50 000 map gives this information. Note also that while brown is used on the 1:25 000 scale to indicate motorways and A roads, on the 1:50 000 scale it indicates B roads.

Do not confuse cuttings with embankments on railways and roads. To a keen eye the difference is obvious – a solid line marks the sharp edge of a cutting.

Scale

Do not neglect this very simple and basic topic.

On the 1:25 000 scale each unit of length *represents* 25 000 units: eg 1 millimetre represents 25 000 millimetres (25 metres). For this reason 1/25 000 is called the **Representative Fraction (RF)** for this scale. An RF of 1/50 000 is obviously *smaller* than 1/25 000. 1:50 000 is thus a smaller scale than 1:25 000.

Map references

The position of any point in Britain can be stated to within one hundred metres by means of the **National Reference Grid**. This is a network of imaginary lines covering the whole country in 100km squares. Each of these squares is subdivided into kilometre squares numbered from west to east (the **easting**) and from south to north (the **northing**).

In the diagram, drawn to 1:50 000 scale, the village of Bolton lies in kilometre square 54 easting and 30 northing. 5430 is the **four-figure reference** identifying this square and thus locating the village within it.

Now imagine square 5430 subdivided into tenths each way, as suggested in the diagram. The symbol for Bolton Church lies about 8 tenths *east* of grid line 54 and about 9 tenths *north* of grid line 30. We can thus quote a **six-figure reference** 54(8)30(9), or simply 548309, to locate the church to within 100m. Similarly, Copper Wood is in square 5731 and Copper Farm is at 574316. *Note: easting always before northing – E before N in the alphabet !*

Give a four-figure reference for (a) Caston village, and a six-figure reference for (b) Caston Church, (c) The Grange, (d) Woodlands, (e) Malt Farm, (f) What is at 565315 ?

Check your answers with the footnote.

Your ability to use four- and six-figure references (often called GRs – **Grid References**) will almost certainly be tested in this way. Furthermore you will be expected to use GRs in your answers to more general questions on the map extract.

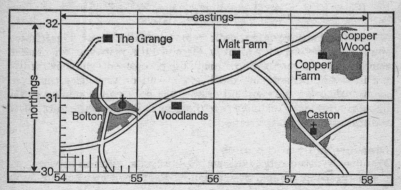

Answers

Compass directions and grid bearings

A mark or two is sometimes allotted to such questions as:

> *What is the grid bearing of Bolton Church (548309) from Malt Farm (563316)?*

Less frequently a simple compass direction is required. In either case the easting grid lines may be taken as running due north-south. Be careful to take your bearing *from* the 'from' point and not *to* it. Both forms of the question are answered in the diagrams.

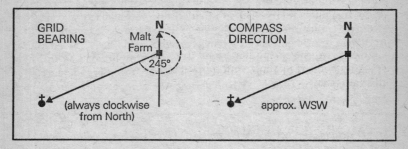

Orientating map and photograph

The map extract is often accompanied by a low-level air photograph covering part of the same area, and a wide variety of questions may arise from this combination (*p146*). Before any such questions can be answered the map must be *orientated*, ie lined up with the view shown. Hence the first question is almost always:

> *In which direction was the camera pointing?*

Look first for three or four prominent features such as a bridge, church spire, railway line, etc; identify them on the map and orientate it roughly. Draw a vertical line through the photo centre and look for two features – one distant, one much closer – on or very near this line; identify them on the map and draw a line on it corresponding to the photo centre line. This line (*from* the near *to* the distant feature) gives the bearing or compass direction.

Measurement of distance

You may be asked simply to state the horizontal distance between two points (probably defined by six-figure GRs) or you may need to know the distance for some other purpose. Proceed as follows:

1 Make a rough estimate by eye, in relation to the kilometre squares crossed or partly crossed by the line you are measuring.

2 Measure more carefully, either by marking off along the folded edge of a sheet of paper or:
3 by 'stepping off' the distance with dividers set to a known distance.
4 In either case, measure both ways and finally compare the answer (converted from map distance to ground distance) with your rough estimate.

Calculation of gradient

Rarely asked for, but very easy to answer with a little practice. Only the *average* gradient between two points is likely to be required, and the method is simply to divide the horizontal distance by the difference in height.

Having measured the horizontal distance as suggested opposite, the essential point is to show your working. This can very well be done in diagram form:

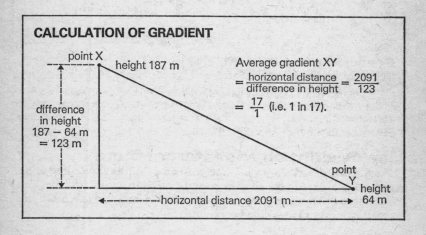

CALCULATION OF GRADIENT

point X — height 187 m

difference in height 187 − 64 m = 123 m

point Y — height 64 m

horizontal distance 2091 m

Average gradient XY

$$= \frac{\text{horizontal distance}}{\text{difference in height}} = \frac{2091}{123}$$

$$= \frac{17}{1} \text{ (i.e. 1 in 17).}$$

Note: the gradient is stated as 1 in 17 without mention of metres or any other unit.

Cross-sections

About half of OS map questions include the drawing of a **cross-section** between two points, usually identified by GRs. Graph paper or a printed framework is often supplied, but you must be prepared to draw your own (see over). This involves using the two means by which altitude is marked on OS maps:

1 **contour lines** joining points of the same height above sea level.
2 **spot heights** – marked points labelled with their height.

To show the relief clearly the vertical scale of a cross-section must usually be exaggerated, but this must not be overdone. If a vertical scale is not suggested in the question, proceed thus:

1:25 000 series   The **vertical interval** (VI) is 25ft – draw cross-lines for each contour, 3mm apart. (NB later sheets have a VI of 10m, or even 5m in very level areas. In these cases draw the cross-lines 4mm apart for each 10m contour.)

1:50 000 series   Most sheets still show the old 50ft contours, renumbered to the nearest metre. The resulting VI is 15 *or* 16 metres. Draw cross-lines 3mm apart for each contour. (NB later sheets have a VI of 10m; in such cases draw cross-lines for each contour 2mm apart.)

To draw a cross-section:

1 join the specified end-points on the map with a pencil line;
2 lay along the line the edge of a folded sheet of paper, and mark off on it the end-points;
3 mark also every contour and spot height crossed or touched by the line, adding the height of each;
4 draw (if not supplied) a framework with a base line exactly the length of the section, and with cross-lines at a V.I. correct for the scale (see previous page);
5 lay the folded paper along the base line, as shown above, and very accurately (using ruler and set-square, if you prefer) transfer each point to its correct level;
6 join up the points with a smooth line.

Map description and interpretation

The exercises described so far test candidates' skills in reading and measuring a map. Almost all map questions test, in addition, the more difficult skill of visualizing the true nature of the land surface shown in the map extract or in a specified part of it.

Physical features

This is the most common topic in questions of this type, eg:
80 Describe the main features of relief and drainage in [a specified area].
81 Describe the physical features of [a specified area].
82 Describe the landscape within [a specified area].

CONSTRUCTING A CROSS-SECTION
(see opposite page)

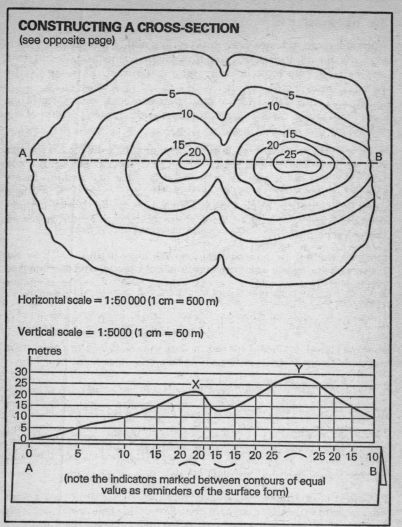

Horizontal scale = 1:50 000 (1 cm = 500 m)

Vertical scale = 1:5000 (1 cm = 50 m)

(note the indicators marked between contours of equal value as reminders of the surface form)

Occasional questions concern **intervisibility**; eg can the house at (*a specified point*) be seen from (*another specified point*)? The answer is usually found by drawing a 'sight line' on a cross section through the two points. In the section above, A and X are intervisible but A and Y are not.

A correct answer obviously depends on accurate identification of the specified points and on accurate measurement and drawing; but only a few minutes can be spared. Practice to combine accuracy with speed is therefore essential.

Such questions test not only map-reading ability but also an under-standing of landforms (Ch 3) and often involve comparing the map with an air photograph. Sometimes they require the drawing of a sketch-map based on the map grid.

This, whether called for or not, is an excellent way to tackle the question. Practise the following procedure with selected portions of any OS 1:25 000 or 1:50 000 map:

—draw a grid at the same scale as the map, or at half the scale if the area is large. Number the grid lines. Using the squares as guides, mark in blue the rivers and streams. Next look for the thickened contours (every fourth contour on the 1:25 000 scale, every fifth on the 1:50 000) and mark them lightly in black. On the higher ground find, mark and num-ber the highest spot heights. Look along the streams to find and mark the lowest points.

—which contour (if any) divides lowland from highland? Show the distinction by *lightly* colouring the highland brown and the lowland green. Is there a great difference of height within the brown area? Show this by darkening the upper levels.

—you should by now be able to distinguish the main features of relief and the contrasting types of scenery into which the area may be divided. Your description must be orderly and logical. What *are* the 'main physical features' to be mentioned? Follow this check list:

1 Upland   Is the area *entirely/mainly/partly/not at all* hilly, or moun-tainous ('Mountainous', in Britain, means over about 600 metres, or *c* 2000 feet)? State the approximate size and location (eg 'the western half', 'the southeastern quarter' etc) of the upland area. What is its average height, and how high are the highest points? Do these represent isolated, outstanding hilltops or peaks, or do they lie on a more or less level plateau? To what extent is the upland dissected by valleys?

2 Valleys   In what general direction do they run, and/or what pattern do they form? Are they narrow or broad? deep or shallow? with steeply or gently sloping sides? straight or winding? flat-bottomed or V-shaped?

3 Streams and rivers *(see also pp42–6)*   Few or many? large or small? with steep or gentle gradient? straight or winding course (interlocking spurs)? flowing in (which?) compass direction? The specified area is often a river valley (p156). In such cases, start by checking whether the stretch of river and valley in the extract can be divided into contrasting sections. If so, make these the basis for your orderly account.

How contours show landforms

Here and overleaf are a few examples of landforms as they appear on a contoured map. The contours are numbered in metres. Check the description in each case by drawing a cross-section along the lines indicated. Find similar patterns of contours on actual O.S. maps. Make sure you can explain, with reference to page 149 if necessary, why contours close together indicate a steep slope.

The map on page 151 illustrates a *cliff* and also, between the two summits, a *col* or *saddle*.

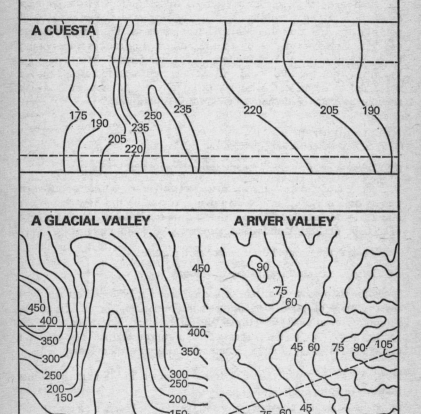

4 Lowland Level or undulating? merging gently or abruptly into highland? lying at what average height above sea level? occupied to what extent by the flood-plain of a river or rivers?

5 Coasts (*see also pp53–5*) Concordant or discordant? generally straight, or broken by bays and headlands, or deeply incut by narrow inlets? marked by erosion or deposition? (Note any features typical of either.) Height of cliffs, width of beaches, estuaries, etc?

To such general descriptions can be added details *based on map information.* Many questions begin 'Using map evidence only . . .' and you must assume that this is intended in all cases. Thus, the presence of lakes or marshes may show that the underlying rock is impervious; the shape of a valley may suggest that it was formed by a glacier; a beach may be of mud or sand. All these are physical features. You are *not* asked to describe the human geography of the area, and so any mention of roads, settlements, fields, etc, is superfluous.

Human geography
This is, nevertheless, a frequent topic, eg:

83 Comment briefly on the human geography of [a specified area].

'Briefly' is a useful hint, for the map probably tells us more about what people do (land use), where they live (settlement) and how they move about (communications) than we have time to set down. Consider each of these points in turn and make an orderly, *concise* statement.

Such questions may, however, be more precise:

84 Describe the land use of [a specified area].

Does the map show an urban or a rural area (or both)? If urban, look for evidence of residential/industrial/commercial/transport/medical/religious/educational/recreational and other uses. These may also be found, of course, in rural areas, but there you should look first for evidence of farming/forestry/mining and quarrying/water storage.

Settlement You must be able to recognize on an OS map the points made in Chapter 8, eg:

85 Describe the site, situation, form and functions of [a specified town].
86 Describe the general distribution of settlement in [a specified area].
87 With the aid of a sketch-map . . . make a division of [a specified area] *into different settlement patterns. Describe, and suggest reasons for, these patterns.*

A. FIELD SKETCH OF STREAM-ERODED HILLSIDE

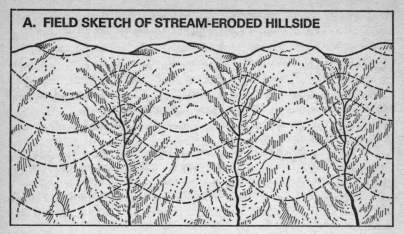

B. CONTOUR MAP OF SAME AREA

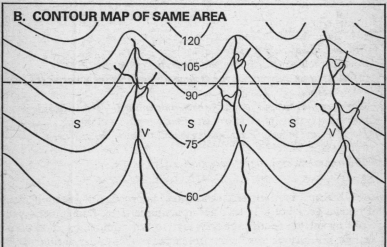

Spurs (S) and valleys (V) are marked by similar kinks in the contour lines. The difference is that the kinks point *upstream in a valley* (lowland cutting into highland) and *downstream on a spur* (highland bulging out into lowland). It is thus possible to tell at a glance the direction of flow of a stream.

Questions of urban 'form' and 'structure' are increasingly common. You may be asked to relate generalized diagrams like that on p133 to a particular town on the map extract. A large-scale air photograph of part of the area is often included. Practice in interpreting air photos, and in relating them to a map, is essential.

Communications Most roads, railways and canals were built to *link* existing settlements as directly as possible. Some modern roads are deliberately built to *bypass* existing settlements. Both these points may be clear from the map.

The influence of relief, and of natural obstacles such as rivers, is an equally important factor. Obstacles may sometimes be overcome (eg by bridges or tunnels) and steep gradients can be eased with cuttings and embankments, yet quite often an indirect route (eg a winding valley) offers a cheaper solution.

Such points will show up clearly on a simple sketch-map drawn as already suggested. This, with one or two paragraphs summarizing the main features involved and locating them with grid references, will answer such questions as:

88 For the railway shown on the map:
    (a) show how its route is related to the relief of the area;
    (b) state three different ways by which the gradient is kept as level
          as possible. (CAM)
89 Compare the routes followed by the main roads with those followed by
    the railways. (LOND)
90 How far, and in what ways, are communications in the map area
    influenced by relief? (SUJB)
91 From map evidence suggest why the canal in square 8779 has no locks,
    while the canal in square 8780 has four sets of locks. (SCOT)

Most OS map questions test candidates' knowledge of both physical and human geography, but always at a simple level. Remember – you are not meant to spend more than five to ten minutes on each part-question. The answer must therefore be fairly obvious, and will usually become so if you relate the wording to the map in a commonsense way. With practice as already suggested, the compulsory OS map question can be a flying start towards a good pass.

Index

Ronald Ridout
Pan Spelling Dictionary   £1.50

John Daintith
A Dictionary of Physical Sciences   £1.50

Stella E. Stiegler
A Dictionary of Earth Sciences   £1.50

E. A. Martin
A Dictionary of Life Sciences   £1.50

Robert Seton Lawrence
A Guide to Speaking in Public   85p

K. G. Thomson and D. S. Bland
A Guide to Letter Writing   £1

For a list of **Pan Study Aids** titles see page two of this book